Real Women's Stories

Real Women's Stories

Stories

2018

Edited by Beth Kallman Werner

Publisher: Author Connections, LLC
Editor: Beth Kallman Werner
Front cover image: Marion Bieber
Front cover design: Peter Cyngot
Book layout design: Suzanne Verheul

ISBNs
978-0-9980201-0-5 (paperback) -- 978-0-9980201-8-1 (hardcover) --
978-0-9980201-9-8 (ePub) -- 978-0-9980201-5-0 (Kindle)

Library of Congress Control Number: 2017915555

"There's a Hole in My Sidewalk" by Portia Nelson has been reprinted on pages 101-102 with permission from Alfred Publishing, LLC.

This is an original print edition of *Real Women's Stories, 2018.*

This book is dedicated to

Esther Kallman

Ellen C. Fletcher

Sarah Peterson

Contents

Mom & Me

by Ava Carmel

Years ago, Mom used to say she wanted to have a pill that she could take when she got old and demented, and didn't want to live any more. Well, even if she had such a pill, she wouldn't be able to find it now.

How can a woman who doesn't recall anybody's name, what day it is, the man she used to live with, or where she left her keys, remember that the soup at lunch yesterday was too salty? Why does a heart keep beating when a tired, shapeless old body, continually racked with pain, has outlived any semblance of quality of life? She's shriveled, confused, and slouched, wearing dull old-lady clothes and living in a retirement home now. Dad died in 1996, and Mom is the last one alive of her generation, on both sides of the family.

My brother and sister-in-law are the only ones who visit regularly—I live in Israel, on the other side of the world, but I'm here for my annual visit. I take a taxi from the airport and reach the retirement home by seven o'clock in the morning. I ride the elevator up to Mom's twelfth floor apartment and open the door.

She's asleep on the couch, clunky white shoes still on, eyes closed, mouth open wide. At first, I'm sure she's dead, and I stand beside her for a moment, until I hear the wheezing of her breath. She opens her eyes and stares at me blankly; then, in a flash of recognition, she cries out, "Ava, you're here!" She's so excited, she's barely coherent.

"Take something to eat," she orders.

I find a box of stale muesli on the counter and open the fridge. It's empty except for a carton of orange juice, eight cans of Ensure, and some small plastic containers filled with leftovers in varying stages of decay. I close the fridge and make myself a cup of tea.

She asks about her three grandchildren and eleven great-grandchildren, and I begin updating, but she quickly loses track of what I'm saying.

1

She slowly wheels her walker, step by step, to the bathroom and then back to the couch. She plops down, leaning backwards and wailing, "Oh, oh, oh, oh my God! Oh my God!" as the pain sears. A woman who was so vehemently secular for her entire life now appeals to God every time she sits down.

Whether the pain is due to a prolapsed bladder or a hernia, the doctor says surgery is out of the question. He prescribed Tylenol, which she takes too often, forgetting she has already taken it. So now it is hidden in one of the upper cupboards and dispensed by Alma, the caregiver.

By now, she has dozed off. A few minutes later, she opens her eyes and tries to get up from the couch, moaning in pain. "Gimme my brush," she commands. "Help me get up."

She wheels herself to the bathroom and sits down, facing the mirror, then begins to apply a thick layer of makeup, tapping it all over her face with the self-assurance and solemnity of a woman who has been doing this for many, many years. Next comes turquoise eye shadow. Black eyeliner. Gray eyebrow pencil. Bright pink lip liner and lipstick. The lines aren't so straight anymore, but the colors are still brash.

I find the entire makeup routine silly, yet fascinating. At ninety-four years old, she still has to "put on a face" before leaving her apartment or before anyone comes to visit, even me. When I was a child, the medicine chest in the bathroom was always overflowing with plastic cases of makeup of all sorts and colors. Mom's hair was jet black. When it started to go gray, she used to jazz it up with silver hairspray. I can still hear the sound of the little ball rattling inside the container when she shook it. A former opera singer, Mom was tall, striking, and melodramatic. She used to wear flashy clothes and costume jewelry; and she was critical, argumentative, and opinionated.

* * *

My mom was the second of two daughters born to Russian Jewish immigrants. She was such a skinny child that the doctor prescribed bacon to fatten her up. Her mother would dutifully go down to the basement to fry it for her. (Bacon was not something one could prepare in the kitchen of a Jewish home.) A good student, she was sent to school, where she excelled at shorthand and penmanship. I always envied her deliberate, flowing script.

She and my father met when he was a member of the Jewish Folk Choir and she was a soloist. They married and honeymooned in New York. I still have a set of silver candlesticks they received as a wedding gift. I was the first of two children, a post–World War II baby born at a time when Jews who survived the Holocaust had children as a way of affirming life. My parents were very much in love and fondly referred to one another as "Poochie."

My brother and I were raised by the book (*Dr. Spock's Baby and Child Care*), fed and toilet-trained on schedule, and spanked for any infringement of the rules. Mom was a suburban housewife—distracted by shopping, talking to her friends on the phone, and reading the three daily newspapers, which were always piled high on the floor beside the couch.

Dad was an immigrant from Poland trying to succeed at business in Canada; he was continually stressed. We often ate macaroni and cheese, TV dinners, or instant mashed potatoes and corned beef in plastic bags you prepared by dropping them into boiling water for three minutes. When dad was diagnosed with high cholesterol, out went the butter and in came the chalk-white margarine in a block with an orange tab on one side. For some odd reason, it wasn't legal to sell margarine that looked like butter, so you had to press the tab and knead the color into the margarine.

Despite the margarine, Dad had multiple heart attacks. After he died, Mom had a gentleman friend who would tell her she was "scintillating." They went to art classes together and she began referring to herself as Margo.

"It's a more appropriate name for signing paintings," she explained to me.

The walls of her apartment are still covered with her artwork—mainly portraits of women. She showed remarkable talent, especially for someone who started painting so late in life.

* * *

Mom dozes off again, so I go down to the lobby to say hello to the staff members and residents. There is a round table with a large vase of flowers near the main entrance, and to the right of that is a seating area with bistro tables and chairs. There are always people mingling near the self-serve hot drinks. I sip my coffee surrounded by early risers, such as the two men who walk their dogs at the same time each morning. One says, "It's a beautiful day," and the other replies, "Every day is a beautiful day."

I enjoy talking to those residents who make efforts. There's a one hundred-and-four-year-old woman who swims fifty laps of the overheated pool every day, and a ninety-nine-year-old man who walks on the treadmill for half an hour every morning. The pool lady has severe arthritis and claims the swimming loosens up her joints.

"Better than taking pills," she says. She scoffs at the majority of residents who have surrendered to old age.

Mom and I spend the rest of the morning catching up. Last year when I was here, the physiotherapist warned her that if she didn't walk up and down the hall with her walker every day, she would lose the use of her legs. So now, though barely mobile, she gets from the bedroom to the bathroom to the living room with a walker. The caregiver takes her down to meals in a wheelchair, and when I'm here, I take her to meals.

At lunchtime, we go down to the dining room and she proudly shows me off to everyone. At home, at sixty-nine, people typically see me as an old lady. Here, I'm relatively young and spry. I strut down the hallway, pushing her wheelchair, head held high, soaking up the admiration from my elderly admirers. Mom introduces me as her ugly daughter, and of course, they all remark how beautiful I am. Yes, in a retirement home I do feel young and beautiful.

One man comes right up to me, a little too close, looks me in the eye and asks if I'm a resident.

"No, I'm Margo's daughter," I reply, nodding toward my mother.

"I don't care whose daughter you are," he replies lasciviously.

Another anticipates my annual visits, comes to the gym when he knows I'll be swimming, and watches me through the window.

Mom sleeps all afternoon while I take my laptop down to the lobby to catch up on emails. She doesn't have Wi-Fi or Internet in her apartment. She never mastered the art of emailing.

We go down to dinner together at five o'clock. I'm not hungry yet, but Mom likes to avoid the rush. She eats at a reserved table with five of her friends. They're thrilled to see me, and I'm sincerely happy to see them all alive and relatively well. I pass around chocolates and they all fuss over me.

After dinner, the evening ritual begins. I know Mom can undress herself, but when I'm here, she becomes helpless. I help her remove her pants and the disposable underwear, then ease her into a new pair. I remove her top, lowering the nightgown over the shapeless mass her body has become. She eases herself onto the bed, crying out. When the pain passes, she removes her hearing aids, puts them in the box on the night table, and lies down. I lift her feet up onto the bed and she turns on her side. I put the little cushion between her knees, arrange the pillow, place the box of tissues within reach, and move her watch to the night table, next to the telephone. I say goodnight, and she says she can't hear me. I tuck her in and wait to see if there's anything I have forgotten.

She falls asleep right away, so I close the door to her room and tiptoe around. Every once in a while, she wakes up and calls out, telling me to do something for her.

"Open the window."

"Dim the light a bit more."

When I was a teenager coming back from a date, I would tiptoe into the house, but she would always hear the door open and call me. She would be lying in bed with Dad, and I would have to endure a cross-examination. *Where did you go? Who did you go with?* I hated it.

The sixties were raging right outside of our split-level home on Pannahill Road. Despite being mostly obedient and subdued at home, I rebelled often, with vengeance. (But that's another story.)

By the third day of my current visit, I'm so bored that I decide to clean out Mom's cupboards and drawers. I find three umbrellas, fourteen pairs of chopsticks, three sets of salad spoons, and three nutcrackers (no nuts). There are almost-empty bottles of fabric softener, nail polish, and makeup remover; nine nail clippers; six thermometers; twelve lipsticks used down to the very end; eight bottles of liquid makeup, no longer liquid; nail files; safety pins. Empty boxes. Empty bags. Empty life.

Since she can't read anymore, I decide to donate the pile of paperback books on the shelf above her bed to the library downstairs. When I tell her, she objects, so I hand her the first book and ask her if she read it.

"I don't remember," she replies. The next book. "I may want to read it again sometime." A book called *Prima Donna*.

"Did you read it?"

"No."

"Then why did you buy it?"

"Because I liked the title."

With nothing to do except read or watch TV, I try to find the humor in my situation and decide to write down what I can recall of the dinner conversation. It doesn't really matter who said what.

"Where's Carol?"

"She said she wouldn't be coming to dinner Wednesday and Thursday."

"She had her colonoscopy this morning."

"Should we phone and ask how she is?"

"I wouldn't phone. She's probably tired."

"I'll call her tomorrow morning."

"Did Brenda return your book yet?"

"No. Yesterday morning she said she would return it in the afternoon and she didn't."

"Did you see her yesterday? She was wearing a hot pink dress."

"Today she didn't come to work."

"If she doesn't return the book, next time I see her, no matter who she's with, I'm going to go right up to her and demand that she return my book. She's had it for over a month, and I want my daughter to read it."

"Ladies, are you ready to order?"

"I'll have a Greek salad, but this time I want lots of olives. Last time there were only two olives in my salad. I don't want the cabbage borscht. They should have cold beet borscht."

"I'll have a mushroom omelet."

"Yesterday I had a BLT and the bacon was so crispy!"

"I'll have the lamb curry with rice."

"Today I was going out, and outside the front door there was a truck parked. Two seedy characters carried a . . . what's it called? A gurney, into the building. On the back of the car it said cremation. I think the name of the company was Tranquil or Tranquility, or something like that. I wonder who died. They said she was from the third floor."

"What did I order?"

"You ordered a grilled cheese sandwich."

"Last night I was taking my makeup off with Pond's Cold Cream..."

"You wear makeup?"

"Only a bit of makeup and some eyebrow pencil. I don't use eyeliner because I can't see."

"Anyway, I use the cold cream to remove the makeup. I usually buy it at Shoppers Drug Mart. I went to Walmart and it was half the price. I've been overpaying for eleven years!"

"What did I order?"

"Grilled cheese."

"Yesterday at lunch the sauce for the spring rolls was too hot. They bought the wrong sauce. Last time they had plum sauce."

"And at lunch today they only gave us two tiny shrimps with no sauce. They had no taste. I should have ordered the shepherd's pie."

"So who's coming to dinner tomorrow?"

"Carol said she wouldn't be coming Wednesday or Thursday."

"But tomorrow's Friday."

"Did Brenda give you your book back yet?"

"No, would you believe it?"

Mom goes to the bathroom every hour or so during the night. She gets up by herself, and with no audience, doesn't let out a sound. At five in the morning, she gets up, dresses herself, and wakes me, telling me to take her to dinner. Her hair is unkempt, she's bewildered and has a wild look in her eyes. Nothing I say can convince her that it's morning. She grabs my arm and clings to me, begging me not to leave her. I'm annoyed, jetlagged, and I want to go swimming. Finally, she begins to calm down, and when Alma comes to give her a shower, she tells her caregiver that I will be taking care of her from now on.

Every evening at seven, Mom watches *Jeopardy!* Surprisingly, she often knows the answers.

Always the dutiful daughter, I'm taking care of her as best I can, but I'm already counting the days until I go back home. I long to go out for a beer or soak in a hot bath with lavender oil, but there's nowhere to go and only a shower stall. I'm still mulling over my childhood. I go out for a long walk, to the mall and back. At every crack in the sidewalk I find myself repeating, "and break your mother's back."

Mom needs to go into a nursing home, which I soon discover is now called long-term care. I broach the subject with her and she is adamantly against it.

"I like it here. I love my apartment, and my friends are here," she says firmly.

Mom moans all morning about the unbearable pain; she can't get up from the couch without help, she's confused and disoriented, but then Elana, the social worker, comes to do an assessment, and Mom's a different person—alert, describing her pain as moderate. She doesn't groan at all during the visit, and in the middle of the assessment, she gets up and wheels herself to the bathroom with no trouble. She assures Elana that she doesn't need any help.

Fortunately, Elana is familiar with Mom's history and explains to her that someday she may need more care and that there is a long waiting list for suitable places. Would she agree to put her name on the waiting list? Mom sees the logic in this and agrees. The subject is no longer taboo.

* * *

From what I can tell, Mom barely drinks 24 oz. of liquid each day, so why does she get up to pee every hour during the night?

She's a consumer of trees, using up boxes of tissues, rolls of toilet paper, and piles of disposable underwear. My brother told me that she recently phoned the drugstore and ordered medication for dry mouth. He kept telling her that if she drank water she wouldn't have a dry mouth, but to no avail.

The next morning, Alma has given Mom a shower (she cried out and moaned the entire time). Now she's sitting on her walker in the bathroom.

"Ava! Ava! You promised to dry my hair."

I make a few futile attempts at blow-drying. Her hair is brittle, and the hairdresser must have used half a can of spray to shape it because now it just lies flat and lifeless. I dry and brush, but it remains limp.

She looks at herself blankly in the mirror for a long moment, then wheels herself step by step to the couch, eases herself down, groaning and crying, "Oh my God!" even before her bottom makes contact with the couch. When the pain eases, I gently lift her legs up and cover them with a woolen shawl. I place the telephone, her glasses case, and the newspaper on her chest. Her feet are swollen and misshapen. I make an appointment with the podiatrist.

Later, we're down at dinner again.

"Are you ladies enjoying your meal?"

"Hi, Di. Yesterday the sauce for the spring rolls was too hot. And the day before, for lunch, there was pastrami on a kaiser bun. The bun was delicious, but there was cheese on the pastrami. If you're going to put cheese on the pastrami, you have to list it on the menu. It's not that we can't eat milk with meat, but we don't."

"In a delicatessen, when you order a pastrami sandwich, the meat is an inch thick. Here they gave us one slice. And you couldn't even taste it, because of the cheese."

"OK, ladies, I'll let the chef know."

"Di, can we have another set of salt and pepper shakers for our table? It's too far to lean over to get them."

"I'll look into it."

"Di, do one of your magic tricks. Benjie, give Di a twenty-dollar bill so he can make it disappear."

"I'm sorry I ordered the lamb. It was better last week."

"My son left me a DVD with a movie he made."
"What's the name of the movie?"
"I don't know."
"What's it about?"
"I don't know."
"Your son makes a movie and you don't ask him what it's called or what it's about?"
"No, I'll watch it and then I'll know."
"So who's coming to dinner tomorrow?"

It's my last evening. I tuck Mom into bed, kiss her on the cheek, and say goodnight. She says, "I love you" and I reply, "I love you too." She has already taken out her hearing aids, so she can't hear the agitation in my voice. Suddenly I'm all tears. I came here, needing so badly to be mothered, and instead, I just spent two weeks mothering her.

I worry about how we'll say goodbye, how she'll react, knowing that it may be the last time we ever see each other.

The next morning I kiss her and leave her sitting in her wheelchair in the lobby, with Alma by her side. I turn and head for the taxi. I look back through the open door and see that she's talking to someone, and has already forgotten that I'm gone.

A Genuine Smile

by Marlena M. Matute

"What happens to this family, stays with this family," might as well be our motto, well at least on my mother's side. I'm not entirely sure why appearances have always been so important, especially to the women. No one could know that there were cracks hiding behind the beautiful façade they'd created—those women were masters at hiding them, teaching the next generation to do what they had done for decades.

I was an unwitting apprentice under the tutelage of my mother while my brother was more like the uninterested inspector, just making sure the cracks didn't spread to the point that a piece of marble would break off and destroy the overall illusion. It was always the three of us against the world, so bringing in someone else was out of the question. I never shared my feelings with anyone and no one bothered to ask, so I kept it all inside until adulthood. After years of hiding my true emotions behind faux smiles, I began to realize that this practice was isolating and destructive, and it was taking a toll on me.

Fall 2013

At twenty-three, I was sure that things were going to fall into place for me. I had just gotten back from Paris, where I'd studied seventeenth- and eighteenth-century châteaux. I had a job as a research assistant/historian for an online research company, and I was completing my final year as a master's student in the history of decorative arts and design. I was anxious, yet ambitious, as I was the first in my family to make it this far.

It was just before Thanksgiving, and I was already looking forward to having those few days off from school to get some classwork done. I don't remember what class I had that day or what I wore, but I do remember being consumed by fear when I saw the sign in front of the house where we'd been renting rooms from Mr. and Mrs. Kazia for the past eight years. It was tied to the handrail of the twisting staircase.

For Sale

Before we moved here, we'd been sleeping in the dining room of my mother's best friend's apartment. My mother never let us work back then; she wanted us to focus on our education. She worked multiple jobs every day of the week, taking what little money her employers were willing to give her in order to provide as much as she could for us. So when the opportunity came to get a space of our own, an actual home, I jumped on it, pitching in all the money that I had received from my sixteenth birthday, a total of $950, for the deposit. It was the first real home I'd ever known, and even with all its quirks, it meant a lot to me. The thought that I would be forced to leave it was disheartening.

"God is on our side," my mother responded, when I sent her a text with my concerns.

"It won't sell, there are way too many things to fix," my brother joked, later that same day, as he peeked over my laptop screen where I was browsing apartment listings.

I'd like to say that I had faith that everything would be alright, but I would be lying. Days I should have spent on classwork were filled with anxious Internet searches, including the following:

17th century France/Versailles
NYFA job classifieds
Homeless shelters
Bueno Royal Palace in Spain
Fighting eviction
Zillow – Apts in East Elmhurst, NY
Zillow – Apts in Jackson Heights, NY
Zillow – Apts in Long Island City, NY
MET Museum careers
Frick Collection careers

Sotheby's careers
Dropping out of grad school with loans

Every day, I would get on the express train in a daze; all this thinking about ways to save my family (and not finding any) kept me distracted. I became less enthusiastic and wasn't as involved in my classes, but I thought I was doing a good job at hiding it—though the amount of times that I heard "Are you okay?" from friends, classmates, and professors clearly demonstrated otherwise.

I couldn't tell anyone about my situation, so I did what I was taught to do: I kept up appearances so that I would be left alone to figure things out for myself. And the only solution that I came up with was dropping out of school midway through my final year. Given everything that was going on, it just made sense. I had the college degree I needed to get full-time employment, while my brother was on an ill-advised break from all adult responsibilities after graduating summa cum laude. He couldn't be bothered with this problem. Yes, I'll admit that I was (and still am) a bit salty about the whole thing.

It was during a dinner of *carne asada* with *arroz con gandules*, a family staple, that I announced, "I'm not registering for classes next semester."

My brother put down his fork and glanced at my mother who gave me this annoyed look as she chewed. It wasn't unusual for me to say something like that, as grad school was difficult for me—I was the only person of color and the only one in my program from a working-class background. My classmates had connections that gave them access to opportunities I desperately wanted. I had to fight twice as hard just to meet them halfway; it was even harder to get the respect of some of my professors. My mother was always quick to remind me that this field was something I chose and that meant fighting for what I wanted. I knew my mother's look meant that she did not want to have that conversation again.

"We don't know what the Kazias are planning on doing with the house and we need to be prepared. I think putting my studies on hold is a good solution. We get more income coming in so we can save up for an apartment, maybe even one with three rooms instead of two."

My mother took a sip of juice. "You're already working now, so that's unnecessary."

"But it's only part time. That's really not going to help much if they decide to kick us out next week."

My brother snorted. "They can't do that; it's illegal. And if they try, we could sue."

I glared at him. "Oh, so we don't have enough money to get an apartment, but we have enough for legal fees?"

"Mrs. Kazia said they are looking for buyers interested in having tenants, so we may not even have to move. So stop with the nonsense."

"This isn't nonsense. We don't know for sure what's going to happen. Who's to say that this new landlord isn't going to harass us like Mr. and Mrs. Kazia do? Or if they decide to get new tenants? What will we do then?"

My mother rolled her eyes.

"You're not quitting school. You only have five months left."

"That's not the point! We need to move and we don't even have half of the money needed for that."

"This apartment is under *my* name, so I'll make that decision when it is needed. You just need to work on your thesis project and graduate. I won't have my daughter be a museum gift-shop cashier when she has the ability to be museum director!"

Knowing there was no other way to convince her, I tried another tactic. "Can we at least ask someone to find out what our options are here?"

"No. We don't beg for help."

"It's not begging. It's asking and—"

"I said no! We will deal with this ourselves. Just like we've always done."

By this point my mother was standing looking down at me, and I didn't look up because I knew that last statement meant the conversation was over.

Later that evening, there was a knock at the door. Mrs. Kazia had come upstairs to let us know that they would be showing the house the following week and that meant coming up to our apartment. My mother set up the time with her while I sat on the sofa, googling "How to buy a house."

A couple of weeks later, I came home from a long study session at the library to find strangers in my house. My mother was on the sofa pretending to watch TV, while my brother stayed in his room playing video games. A multigenerational Hispanic family came to tour the house late in the evening, and for some reason, decided to tour our apartment for an hour. I should point out that our apartment wasn't big. It was made up of three rooms aligned in a row, with the closet-sized bathroom and the kitchen separated by a wall. This parade of lookers became the norm every Wednesday around five in the afternoon, from December to March. Each visit ended with Mr. Kazia subtly mentioning that there was a bid on the house with a no-tenants clause, but that he was doing the Christian thing and trying to find a buyer who would have tenants. That turned out to be a lie. In the new year, Mrs. Kazia asked us if we knew that Home Depot had moving boxes for an affordable price, which was a sign that we should start packing.

Spring 2014

By this point I had already changed tactics. Since my mother wouldn't listen to my pleas for help, I searched hard for an internship or fellowship in art history, design, or decorative arts that could potentially lead to a full-time position in June. I submitted my résumé to a bunch of places and received an answer from only one—Christie's Auctions & Private Sales. It was unpaid, yet it fulfilled my requirements: (1) it took the place of a class on my schedule, so I had less schoolwork to get done, (2) it gave me the work experience necessary to enter this competitive field, and (3) it was my "in" to an organization that would hopefully lead to a full-time job.

I was working two part-time jobs and going to school full-time, working on my master's thesis while apartment and job hunting on the down-low, and volunteering my technical expertise for a women's empowerment nonprofit. To say I was being pulled in many directions would be putting it lightly. I kept myself busy, working hard to ensure that I graduated with honors and had a job waiting for me so that the threat of homelessness would become a distant memory. I put tremendous pressure on myself, so it shouldn't be surprising that the negative thoughts began to win the battle in my mind.

Even as I slipped deeper into depression, my determination never wavered. I attended my classes (though I was distracted by my slipping grades) and took great care to encourage the women in the nonprofit workshops I was facilitating. It was after one such event that I found myself telling a group of young women that they should always consider reaching out to a friend when they are dealing with something difficult. I caught myself thinking that I was a hypocrite, since I would never do the very thing I was suggesting. Thankfully, two of the charter members of the organization, Belinda and Andrea, were also leading this particular event and they picked up the slack when I faltered.

Later on, the three of us sat and talked for an hour, which was normal for us, but that night I was suffocating beneath the forced smile I'd worn for the evening. I couldn't keep it to myself anymore. I found myself yelling, "Would either of you consider buying a house?"

Belinda and Andrea both knew that the house had been up for sale. Belinda was the first to break the silence, saying, "I thought you were moving."

I shook my head. "We have no place to go."

Andrea turned toward me. "Has the house sold yet?"

"No, there have been offers, but nothing has stuck yet. Can you buy it? I'll buy it back from you, I swear. I just need some time to get the money."

I kept looking everywhere but at them—I'd just broken a major family rule, and I didn't know what to do with myself.

Andrea leaned back and crossed her arms. "Do you think Eleanor could help?"

"Maybe. She does own quite a bit of property, so she might want the house or know someone who is renting," Belinda said, as she took a sip from her water bottle before turning her attention to me. "Hey, it's going to be okay. We can't buy the house, but there is no reason why we can't help in other ways."

16

Andrea tugged on my arm so that I would give her my attention. "Belinda's right," she smiled. "Don't worry. We got this."

I sat there in awe. I wasn't expecting anything from them, yet here they were, offering me help. Tearfully, I found myself smiling and said, "I'm sorry to bother you with this, but thank you."

Andrea scoffed. "Bother? You're our friend. You should have told us sooner. And no tears, missy."

Belinda and Andrea were true to their word. Every day, I received an email with apartment listings. They also introduced me to their individual professional networks and pushed me to broaden my job search beyond my field of study, pointing out the skills I had for writing and social media.

Belinda even went so far as to finance my ticket to attend the nonprofit's annual international conference, taking place that year in Costa Rica. I had no intention of attending because of my full work schedule and the looming deadline for my master's thesis. I declined at every turn, citing my lack of funds to pay her back. Nevertheless, I found myself on a plane that Easter weekend. I had nothing prepared for my workshop and nothing to show for weeks of research for my master's exam paper. I had packed my notes and laptop, though I wouldn't be allowed to touch them.

Our first night there, we had a meeting to share our thoughts on the upcoming work. Everyone had a turn, and most kept it brief because it was late and we had been traveling all day. Then it was my turn. I took a chance and told them that I had nothing prepared, and I didn't believe I would be able to do a good job of facilitating a workshop about depression and anxiety, considering that I was dealing with both of those things. Trying to regain my composure, I ended my statement by asking for ideas for my workshop. At first, I didn't get any. What I got instead was an interrogation that ended with me having an anxiety attack because I was forced to share the unspoken truth—I didn't know if I would have a home to return to.

The ladies immediately came to my aid, giving me ideas for the workshop and reminding me that even in my most vulnerable state, I could help empower women. One team member, Sasha, who is a social worker, told me about a federal housing program my family might qualify for and the steps for applying to it. For the first time in months, I felt hope. The sad part was that it wasn't a feeling I could share with my family; after all, they were set in their ways.

Even after all my determination and the help from my friends, we ended up homeless for a second time. Two days after receiving my graduate degree, I had to throw away furniture, clothes, and other belongings that didn't fit into storage. For the most part, I got to keep only my books and my clothes. It was hard to take. The three of us started moving at six in the morning and kept going well into the next day. At around one in the morning, I found myself packing up the truck while I sobbed, asking God why we were being punished like this after he had blessed us with a home in the first place.

Here's something people don't tell you: being homeless is more expensive than if you're not. Every time I mention that, people are shocked, but it's the truth. When we finally said goodbye to that small shotgun apartment, I had about $6,000 to my name, funds that I had saved over the last year and a half. In just three months, I was down to $2,000. Between paying for the storage space that housed the belongings we managed to keep and buying food (since we didn't have access to a kitchen), our funds ran out quickly. It was a troublesome reality, since typically you need at least two or three months' rent to get an apartment in New York City. When I finally got word that there was an apartment we could move into, I didn't have enough to pay for it and neither did my mother. She had resigned herself to the idea that we might not have a home for quite some time, and hadn't looked into any options. However, with less than a week to accept the apartment, Andrea came up with a solution—reaching out to people who could help.

The night before we were set to hand in our deposit, I gave my mother an envelope with a check for the exact amount we needed.

When she opened it, her eyes widened in surprise and she asked me, "What did you do?"

I smiled, genuinely, and said, "What I had to."

By reaching out, I became able to break those disruptive cycles. I stood up to people I once followed without question—people I look up to and respect. I'll admit that going against my mother's wishes wasn't an easy decision, but it was the right one. It would be years before I would share this story with her. It's been almost four years since that fall day, and we still disagree about our family's practice of keeping everything secret.

The fact remains, you can't expect people to know what you're going through if you don't say anything. We all need someone to lean on from time to time, because you'll only get so far on your own. I was forced to learn that the hard way, but it taught me the power that can come from working together, especially with other women—women supporting women, not for personal gain or accomplishment, just being human.

The Choice

by Crispin McKay

She sits on the exam table, legs swinging, as I walk through the door. She watches me, her stare as clinical as the white walls and stainless steel around us. I introduce myself and hold out my hand. She shakes it and I notice her eyelashes, caked with mascara and standing out from her blue eyes like rays drawn in thick, black marker. She holds my gaze. Riveted, I reach behind me to wheel the stool over and sit.

"Help me," she says, without wavering.

"How old are you, Kylie?" I ask softly, and I know the answer but hope it isn't true. As I watch her, I am thinking about my medical training from decades ago, when I was a student. Young. Fresh. Back when I thought that a doctor's job would be to brilliantly diagnose and heroically save lives—and when I first learned to take patient histories: *Don't ask leading questions*, my professors always said, *if you want accurate information. Say, Can you characterize the pain? Don't say, Is it a burning pain?* With Kylie I want to ask, *Surely you're older than thirteen?*

"Thirteen," she says, as I notice the baby fat spilling over her jeans.

I sit quietly, maintaining a neutral expression. My throat knots and my heart pounds so hard that I think my chin must be bobbing with it. I breathe. In. Out. In. Out.

"Help me," she says again.

I blow air through my pursed lips before I can stop myself, and then I ask Kylie about her life. She is just finishing ninth grade at Frances Longer Middle School and lives with her mother in an apartment in the southwest section of the city. The wrong section—the one with street-parked hoopty rides and graffiti-tagged walls, where the only grass is what has struggled up through the cracks in the cement, persistent and indomitable like the families on the block. I endure her stare, feeling defensive as I ask about drugs and alcohol. *I ask every teen*, I want to say. Finally, I ask how this happened.

"A boy," she says.

"How old?" I ask, then pause for an answer. "A boy you know?"

"I told the other doctor all this," Kylie sighs.

I know she has. The other doctor left me a warning message about referring Kylie for a procedure that is against the law in most states: a pregnancy termination in an unemancipated minor without a parent's consent. I recall listening to the message, wrapping the telephone cord around my fingers, feeling slightly panicked, hoping the girl wouldn't show up. *The father is another kid,* my colleague had said, *Fourteen.* He didn't suspect sexual assault. Not an older boy, then. Or a teacher. Or a family member. Just two kids after school sprawled out on a mattress in an empty apartment. And then an unintended result. *The girl is young, but on it,* my colleague had said; she had figured it out when she was only six weeks along.

"Tell me," I say quietly, meeting Kylie's eyes. "I need to hear it all from you." Not because it will affect my decision, but so I can be sure she is safe. I am already thinking about how to protect this girl if I decide I have to call the police.

The door clicks behind me as I step into the hallway. Leaning against the wall, I stare at the speckles on the linoleum, my hands jammed into the pockets of my white coat. The knot in my throat expands, first through my chest, then to my arms and hands. It burns like poison, like I always imagined tetanus would, as it oozed out from a rusty nail. This was no assault, just a girl with too much free time and too little adult presence, with tenuous boundaries unable to contain her as she searches for love and affection. And approval. As I myself had searched when I was her age, a time when even lustful, impersonal attention—the infatuation of a teenage boy—was better than the emotional loneliness of home.

And yet, even now, as a woman and a physician, the need for approval tugs. I am self-absorbed, worrying about how this procedure will affect me and my career. What if Kylie's story leaks out? What would my colleagues think of me? What if there are complications? The headlines will scream: Botched Abortion Maims Teen. The phone calls, the cyberbullying. *Would I lose my job? My medical license? Go to jail?* And finally, what we all quietly wonder, but never speak, *Will the next fanatical bullet find my chest?*

Shame burns my cheeks as I recognize the temptation to choose the comfortable option, the one that makes me feel safe. Usually when I have this internal discussion, it's about convincing myself to do less, to *not* order the extra test or medication, like the chest X-ray for the upper respiratory infection that I know is not pneumonia. Or the lumbar puncture for the teen with influenza. Or the antibiotic for the kid's cold because the mother is demanding it. Because it's not about what the patient has and needs, it's about me not worrying later, head on my pillow staring up at the dark . . . thinking about the patient having that rare condition or the patient liking me or even filing a law suit. In Kylie's case, my self-interest is nudging me toward withholding the intervention she wants.

I imagine myself as a teen, alone and pregnant. Like an Andrew Wyeth painting, staring out through my filmy bedroom curtains with only my dog and the cows' mournful lowing to keep me company. Would I have reached out before it was too late? Would I have finished high school? Gone to college? Medical school? Become the doctor that I am, charged with helping this child?

As willful and seductive as it was, surprising me with its determination and heat, my own teen body was never pregnant. A memory from my youth, so different from Kylie's, flashes in front of me. I am looking down past my red halter top and cut-off jeans, watching my scuffed Keds swipe the kickstand and peddle me over the dirt and cracked macadam, through rutted, fallow fields to the clinic below River Street. The pills bounce and rattle in a brown paper bag as I ride home. I hide them inside my stuffed bear's paisley jacket and pop one out of the foil each day, swallowing it as I slide a barrette through my curls.

Kylie pushes her way into my thoughts. She scares me. I can manage a seizure or a stroke or a cardiac arrest. But thirteen and pregnant? I think about the Hippocratic oath: First do no harm. And I wonder, which decision is the harmful one? A pregnancy would ravage Kylie's young body, with a high risk of complications like severe hypertension and preeclampsia. Her child could be premature or could even die. And if it were healthy, would it then face Kylie's life? Raised by a single struggling parent, absent due to night shifts or double shifts or a boyfriend or maybe even methamphetamine—a mother whose consistent absence somehow implies consent.

If I try to reach Kylie's mother or try to delay a week, Kylie might vanish into the ether where teens go, lost to me and lost to the chance to restart her life. If I complete the procedure, will the decision haunt Kylie for the rest of her life? Will she lament that she was too young to make such a choice and wonder what might have been?

A familiar anxiety accompanies choices like this—choices with monumental and far-reaching consequences that I don't have time to think about in those few moments when I must decide whether to act, whether to jam in a chest tube that might re-expand a lung, or launch into compressions that will restart a heart. Or whether to remove some cells that will alter the course of a young woman's life.

Leaning against the door jam, I scan the ceiling and then the bare walls, searching for a distraction, some relief. My eyes settle on the picture taped over my medical assistant's desk, a daughter's Magic-Marker portrait of her mother. Thick black lines radiate out from blue eyes. They are my medical assistant's eyes. But they become Kylie's eyes, holding me with her resolute gaze. These eyes tell me the answer. I know suddenly what Kylie knew when she arrived at the clinic—that I can't deny her a new start, that it is *her* body and she knows what she needs. Straightening, I pull my hands out of my pockets and reach for the door. I pause, resting my fingers on the handle, acknowledging the rare feeling of peace and confidence. I can face Kylie and my peers, and my pillow tonight, without racing thoughts and worry. Isn't this why I provide terminations? To help women—and girls—claim dominion over their own bodies.

Kylie watches me as I walk back into the room, still unwavering. I pull the curtain around us. I pull the stirrups out from the exam table, unfold them, and slip a flowered oven mitt onto each end to make them more comfortable on her heels.

"Put your feet here," I say, meeting her eyes as I wheel my stool closer and squeeze her hand. The sanitary paper crinkles as Kylie scoots closer to the table's edge. Then I feel it, as much as I see it, the way she exhales and lifts her feet into the mitts. Kylie relaxes for the first time as she closes her eyes and rolls back onto the exam table.

A Bundle of Love and Joy

by Regina Murphy-Keith

My name is Regina Murphy-Keith. I'm about to share the extraordinary story of my adoption. During the Vietnam War, when I was eighteen months old, two special people, Peter and Eileen Murphy, welcomed me into their loving family. I instantly gained two older brothers, Kevin and Tom, and went from being a Vietnamese baby to an Irish American baby, headed to the United States of America. My short life had changed forever.

My Vietnamese name was Nguyen Thi Thom. One of many children orphaned during the Vietnam War, I was found in 1969 after being abandoned south of Da Nang. Sister Angela and the other nuns took good care of us at the Sacred Heart Orphanage.

I've asked my father, retired United States Marine Corps Chief Warrant Officer 4 Peter Murphy, to share his recollections of the time. These are his memories:

I was a career marine and came up through the ranks. I was married to Eileen Ormond and had two biological sons: Kevin, born in January 1960, and Tom, born in November 1962. I returned from Vietnam to Hawaii, and Eileen and I talked about adopting a child from Vietnam. All my brothers and sisters had many children, and Eileen wanted a daughter. It was destined that we adopt a little baby girl.

When I returned to Vietnam, I went to the Sacred Heart Orphanage, which I had found by chance, and told Sister Angela, the nun in charge, that my wife and I would like to adopt a little girl. Sister Angela was elated, and she went into the infirmary where the infants were kept under netting. I discovered the orphanage needed help with the mere essentials: food, clothing, and medical and health items. My fellow marines and I began acquiring the necessary items for the orphanage from various sources and made deliveries on a regular basis.

I went to the orphanage one day, and Regina was very sick. Without any greetings, Sister Angela told me, "Take this baby to a hospital." I said to myself, "Whoa. How am I going to do that?" It was late afternoon, and movement on the roads was prohibited after sundown. I put Regina in my jeep and drove five or six miles to the 95th evacuation hospital. They were overwhelmed with military patients and civilians, and could not help her, but the doctor put me in contact with a German missionary clinic that cared for injured children. Coincidently, the clinic was located very near the orphanage. I arrived there without incident, rang the doorbell, and a strapping man opened the door. He took Regina out of my arms and slammed the door in my face.

The next day, I told Sister Angela what had happened. She told me the German missionaries did not want any affiliation with the US military for fear of reprisals from the Vietcong. I managed to visit Regina wearing civilian garb. The missionaries tethered her in a crib lined with foil for twenty-one days, to treat her for amoebic dysentery. They fed her German baby food, and she started to heal.

I asked Eileen to send a few cases of American baby food to me, to help the missionaries and the other babies they cared for. Eileen asked some of the returning servicemen if they would sponsor the baby food shipment. At least twenty (from the army, marines, and navy) volunteered to carry the baby food back to Vietnam in their personal baggage. According to Eileen, they were all really happy to do it.

Regina grew healthier and was finally released back to the orphanage. I visited regularly when I finished work and brought her back to my camp area on the weekends. Sister Angela always provided me with the best (tattered) clothes available for Regina. Her diapers were made from soft rags; there was nothing like Pampers and such over there.

My marine buddies started a potty-training effort. We found a little pail, similar to a beach bucket, and put Regina on it. She was not happy about it, but after a while, she got the knack of using it. In retrospect, it was fun for me and the other guys. It took our minds off the conflict that surrounded us. On several occasions, we had to wrap Regina in a flak jacket (body armor) and bring her into our homemade bunker during rocket attacks. I returned Regina to Sister Angela on Sunday afternoons, and the nun was always very happy to see her again.

As Regina grew, she was taken out of the infirmary and put with the other orphans in the open-air barracks. There were twenty or twenty-five other infants Regina's age. The cribs were lined with straw mats and slightly tilted to facilitate the drainage of urine during the night. Sister Angela and the other nuns cared for the babies' needs on a big table, which accommodated ten or twelve infants at a time. Mass diaper changing happened regularly. At meal times, ten or twelve kids were lined up on a bench and fed from a single bowl with a single spoon—mainly rice and broth or whatever the nuns received from the military base mess halls. From time to time, my buddies and I purloined meat from the army, which was put into the rice–broth concoction. The nuns did the best they could with what they had on hand at the time.

The adoption process, meanwhile, took several months. I had to hire a lawyer to acquire all of the necessary documentation, a lot of which had been lost or misplaced because of the ongoing conflict. Affidavits were required when certain documents could not be found. Once everything was complete, I took Regina to Saigon to obtain her exit visa. We flew there in a vintage World War II aircraft that was not pressurized. Regina cried in pain upon takeoff, but there was nothing I could do, and the pressure finally subsided just before we landed.

I was instructed to leave Vietnam within five days of receiving the exit visa. At the time, I was in the ninth month of a thirteen-month tour of duty. I contacted the command adjutant, a major by the name of Angel, and explained the situation. He called his counterpart in Washington, DC, and permission was granted for me to leave with Regina within the allotted time frame. We took off from Da Nang in a Boeing 707 and arrived in Hawaii ten hours later. Eileen, Kevin, and Tom were waiting for us. I asked the customs official for permission to pass Regina over to Eileen and the boys while I cleared customs. Permission was granted and a new chapter began for all of us.

We traveled as a family on a nonstop flight to New York. Regina became dehydrated on the flight and started convulsing when we arrived *at JFK airport. I was able to ice her down at the infirmary, and she recovered in a very short time. As we were leaving the airport, we unexpectedly ran into my brother, Jack. We hadn't seen each other in over four years, so it was exciting to run into him, to say the least. As a bonus, he drove all of us to Yonkers to visit the entire Murphy clan.*

Regina Murphy-Keith: Meeting the Extended Family in the United States

Joining this family, I suddenly had not just parents and brothers, but also grandparents, aunts, uncles, and cousins. They all welcomed me. Grandpa Murphy especially loved me because I ate everything that was put in front of me. Nothing went to waste.

In the summers, I visited family in Connecticut and New York State. My cousin Colleen remembers some funny things about my dad:

He used to raise his voice and say, 'If you don't shape up, Jeannie, I'm sending you back to Hanoi!' We were all dumbfounded and speechless to hear this and felt a little protective over you. Of course, it was meant in jest and only your dad could pull it off.

Our family get-togethers were always a blast. On one Virginia Beach family reunion, the older cousins gathered on the beach and your dad was the guest of honor. We asked Uncle Pete a lot of questions and everyone listened silently while he told us about the war, life, and adopting you. Uncle Pete got choked up when he talked about you. You give him the most joy!"

My dad and I have a great relationship. He refers to us as "budzos." When I was younger, he used to take me on road trips. We'd jump in the car and just drive. We always ended up going down to the ocean, at the end of Roosevelt Avenue. We stood there and smelled the salty air and watched the water crash over the jetty.

Another destination was the Oakhurst Bar on the corner of Monmouth Road and West Park Avenue. (Today, it's a pizza parlor.) I'd sit at the U-shaped bar and have a soda and a Slim Jim. I learned how to play shuffleboard and darts hanging out there. I'm rusty now, but I still enjoy playing shuffleboard at the VFW (Veterans of Foreign Wars—a national organization that advocates for veterans, with local community centers around the United States).

The Oakhurst Bar on Monmouth Road was one of Dad's favorites. I'm not sure if he ever told my mother he was taking me to a bar, but I'm sure if she'd known at the time, she never would have let him. What would people say about a man bringing his child into a dingy bar? I didn't care. I loved going to that dingy bar and spending time with Dad. As I got older, we took fewer and fewer road trips. I was consumed with school, sports, and other activities, but I'll always remember those drives.

Dad and Mom are total opposites. He's tall and she's short. Dad is an extrovert with a loud, raucous voice, while Mom is an introvert with a quiet demeanor. She'd rather stay home with a good book than go out. Dad's usually the center of attention at a party. I truly believe they are soul mates. One wouldn't be able to live without the other. It's true: opposites do attract, as the saying goes.

My mom recently shared her memory of when I first arrived in the United States:

The summer of 1971 was an exciting time. Peter was finally coming home with Regina after a nine-month tour of duty in Vietnam. I felt all types of emotions when the boys and I went to meet them at the airport: happy, excited, and a little anxious. My little girl was coming home!

She was so cute, and I couldn't wait for the rest of the family to meet her. I bought her a sweet rose-colored, corduroy outfit. When we got home from the airport, Regina was crawling around and she encountered the shag rug in the living room. She started crying and became hysterical. Peter picked her up and handed her to me. Her little arms gave me the biggest hug ever. It was such a small incident, but it still remains clear in my mind today. I also remember the boys doting over her.

That summer at the Murphy house was like Christmas—I bought so many outfits for her. Peter said she wore an eighteen-month size, but she was much smaller than that. Needless to say, we had to go shopping.

Shopping with Mom was something I used to look forward to. It was fun to pick out new clothes together. For birthdays or Christmas, Mom would put gifts away months in advance and then forget about them and shop again.

Mom and I share a special bond. As a young child, I loved sitting on her lap when she was relaxing on the couch. She would sing a lullaby and rock me back and forth. I will cherish those special moments forever.

My mother is a sweet woman, but she has a strict side, too. Luckily, she didn't have to show it to me very often, but my brothers were a different story. My relationship with Kevin and Tom was fairly typical. They picked on me like older brothers do. They also protected me if anyone tried to mess with me. I was a tomboy growing up. In a family with two boys, I felt like one of them. I never wanted to wear dresses, or play with dolls or play with the other girls in our neighborhood. It was more fun playing with my brothers. We played outside, and on rainy days, we moved all of the furniture in the living room and played football with a rolled-up sock. We put all the pillows on each end of the room to make end zones.

Sometimes, when Kevin and I were together, he wanted to see people's reactions when he told them we were brother and sister. Most of the time, people thought we were pulling their legs because we don't look anything alike. Other times, they were intrigued and wanted to know our story. I love my brother, but it got to be a pain explaining it all the time. He thought it was funny, but sometimes I wanted to bash him over the head.

When he grew up, Kevin served in the marine corps and was sometimes stationed overseas. I was always happy when he came home to visit and brought gifts from wherever he had been. I remember a particular jacket in Marine Corps red and gold. On the back, it said, "My big brother is a marine," and there was a bulldog embroidered on it. I was proud that he was my big brother and a marine! We've always been close and still are today.

Tom is the comedian in our family. He always tries to make people laugh when they are sad. He used to pretend to fall and hit his head on the edge of the table, which made our mother crazy. She fell for it every time. He frequently used comedy or magic to get himself out of trouble. Even today, he still pretends to fall and hit his head, and our mom still falls for it. I guess it never gets old.

Tom recently shared his memory of the first time he met me:

Regina Marie Murphy—born July 15, 1969. I helped choose the date. The orphanage didn't have any birth documents. When Mom told me I was going to have a baby sister, I was seven years old and excited. Kevin, Mom, and I were waiting on the tarmac at Hickam Air Force Base when the massive cargo plane arrived, and there was Dad, holding a little girl. You were beautiful! It was the coolest thing to have a baby sister and be a big brother. I was there to protect you. I always helped Mom when she needed me. You were a very good baby, too!

For a few years, we lived near the water in Beaufort, South Carolina. Our property had a dock, and friends with boats came to visit all the time. This was where I learned to swim.

I had a great childhood because my family was close, our parents gave us many varied experiences, and throughout my school years I was on a soccer team with good friends, and we had a lot of proud victories. My mom and dad were always on the sidelines cheering.

Just recently, my friend Janet shared a memory from our childhood on Facebook:

I remember Murph's dad coming to our games. He stood near the goal that Murph was guarding as if her life depended on it. One time, we played in a tournament and had a bench-clearing brawl, which was not the norm. We were not fighters. I remember Murph's dad giving us all water and trying to calm us down. I recall his calming voice, gently telling everyone that we needed to regroup.

It's funny because I played soccer with Murph for years and had no idea that she was adopted. She didn't talk about it, and her parents were just her parents. I think that is proof of my belief that blood does not make a parent, love does.

I've been friends with Jennifer since sophomore year in high school. She is beautiful, kind, caring, and hilarious. It was her idea to introduce me to her best guy friend, Dave. We went to see fireworks over the Fourth of July weekend, and ended up dating all through high school. Fast forward seven years later, Dave and I were married on September 6, 1992, which is also my parents' anniversary. We started a deli and catering business in Brick, New Jersey, and rented a tiny house. The deli lasted four years and the catering side of our business is still booming today.

Now we live in Toms River. We have two beautiful, amazing, intelligent daughters. Our oldest, Jordan, is the perfect mix of Dave and me. She attended a prestigious honors program for marine biology in high school, and now studies marine sciences at college. Her goal is to protect and save all marine life.

Jordan has a big heart. She knows how fortunate she is and doesn't take anything for granted.

Our youngest daughter, Rebecca, has beautiful, long, straight hair and a gorgeous smile. She has been on the high honor roll, on the student council, and on the volleyball and softball teams. During the summer, she goes to surfing camp and is currently studying to be a certified, open-water diver. We will all be able to go scuba diving together on our next vacation.

Our family was planning a trip to Asia with a stop in Vietnam, near my birthplace. A coworker of mine did some research and discovered that Sacred Heart Orphanage no longer existed. Then, a man named Dan Brown emailed me the orphanage's roster with all the orphans' names and the dates when they left the facility. Dan had been at Sacred Heart from 1972 to 1974 and became a valuable source of information. I quickly found my own name on the list—I was number 578.

Dan also gave me the name of a nun, Sister Catherine, who was ten years old back in 1971. She had been studying to become a nun when I was there. I reached out to her, and we communicated before meeting.

Asia: The Trip of a Lifetime

Dave, Rebecca, Jordan, and I were joined by Dave's mother on a trip of a lifetime to the beautiful country I left as a baby in 1971. I carefully documented our trip, including the many beautiful locations and fun activities, as well as the culture and food, but most importantly, the unbelievable and extraordinary reunion in Vietnam.

Hanoi, Vietnam

Our flight landed in Hanoi and we were excited to be there. As soon as we got off the plane, I FaceTimed Dad so he could see that we had arrived. Being back in Vietnam for the first time in so many years was an overwhelming feeling.

We spent the next day sightseeing with our tour guide, Thom. The traffic was fast moving; there were a lot of people riding scooters. We saw as many as four people on one scooter, and sometimes the rider was holding a dog. I thought for sure that we were going to get hit or we'd hit someone else. We saw the government and parliament buildings on the way to the Ho Chi Minh Mausoleum, and a lot of people wore masks because of the terrible air quality.

During the tour, Thom told me the meaning of my name: Nguyen means "family," Thi means "female," and Thom means "perfume."

Sa Pa

Next stop, Sa Pa, a tiny town in the Hoang Lien Son mountains was a five-hour drive north from Hanoi. It overlooks terraced rice fields, and the town's population is made up of hill tribes.

Our tour guide, Tien, took us to see the China–Vietnam border. For lunch, we visited the house of Tien's friend, a couple with two adorable children. They sold scarves in the front of their house, which had been turned into a store. In the back of the house, there was a chair for the dental patients, as the husband is a dentist. It was a simple and modest home, but welcoming.

Tien's friend and his wife moved all the furniture and unrolled a mat for us to sit on. They served a traditional hot pot made with broth, different types of greens, mushrooms, pigeon eggs, pork, chicken, and chicken feet. They served homemade plum wine in tiny little shot glasses. Our host refilled Dave and Tien's glasses many times and shook hands after each drink. After the meal, they served us strong green tea. It was all very good and fun to experience with everyone. It was an honor to be invited into our host's home.

The next day, we took a two-hour walk to visit two villages. Women walked alongside of us and persistently tried to sell their items, speaking English very well. The people who live in the villages lead a simple farming life. Many crops are grown on the mountainside—green tea, rice, pineapples, orchids, sugar cane, bamboo, and coconuts. We saw water buffalo, cows, pigs, and a lot of stray dogs. The scenery was breathtaking.

Da Nang and Sister Catherine

Our flight from Hanoi to Da Nang was an hour long, and when we got to the hotel, Dave and I walked down to the famous China Beach. (There's a picture somewhere of me as a baby, sitting on that beach under an umbrella, with a rib in one hand.)

Finally, the big day arrived. Our tour guide and Sister Catherine were waiting for us in the lobby. We set out for the building where the old orphanage had been.

We FaceTimed Dad again, so he could see and speak with Sister Catherine. (It's amazing that technology allows us to do that!) Being in front of the building where my dad found me as a baby was exhilarating.

Sister Catherine showed us Sister Angela's name on the remembrance wall, and led us in a prayer.

As we walked through the nearby preschool, Sister Catherine told us about its history and showed us where she lived. Before we left, we gave Sister Catherine a donation and took pictures with her.

It was truly an amazing experience to go back to where I came from and see everything first-hand. I was happy to have my husband, mother-in-law, and daughters with me on this monumental trip. It was an adventure I will never forget.

Since we got home, I recently received an incredible email from Sister Catherine:

> *My dearest Regina,*
>
> *I would like to thank you very much for visiting me and your old place. I was so happy to see you and your family. It is a miracle to me.*
>
> *When I was ten years old, I entered the convent to learn how to become a sister. I wanted to be a servant of God, to heal and love people because they are children of God and created by God. So, my dream came true.*
>
> *When you were a baby, I was there under the leadership of my superior, Sister Angela, to give baths and feed meals. She guided me to become Sister Catherine today.*
>
> *Regina, I think of you, your family, your father and your mother-in-law in my daily prayers. I emailed Daniel Brown already. He was very happy to receive news from me. Rest assured, your family's picture and Daniel's are on my desk so I*

never forget all of you in my heart and prayers. May God bless you to be in good health always.

I miss and love you. Thank you very much for everything that you gave me. Our children like the things you gave them. Bye bye.

Thanks,

Sr. Catherine Men

I'd like to thank my parents, who are two very special people. They've given me a life of unconditional love, and I would not be the person I am today without them. I would also like to thank my mother-in-law, Amy, my wonderful husband, David, and Jordan and Becca, our two amazing daughters, for their love and support. I love that we got to experience Vietnam together as a family.

A Victory Over Violence

by Nancy Salamone

Picture a well-dressed woman at the top of her game in a Wall Street financial office. On the surface, it seems like another ordinary day at work. She is taking meetings, talking to clients, and responding to email—doing what she does every day. But this day, which began just like any other, won't be ordinary at all. Why? Because she recently left her abusive husband, and she's scared to death that he will come to the office to harass her.

She gives a picture of him to the building security guards, so that if he does show up he won't be allowed in. Well, he does show up. He walks right into the lobby and won't leave until the guards threaten to call the police.

There are a few things you should know about this woman:

- She is a successful marketing executive who has lived in fear for all of her twenty-year marriage.

- Until this day at work, she's never told anyone what she's been going through. She is one of millions of women across the country who are tremendous achievers in their work while silently enduring domestic violence at home, and never saying a word.

- She is me.

When you think of the face of domestic violence, all you need to do is look around you. It can happen to anyone regardless of race, gender, education, religion, or socioeconomic status.

After twenty years of abuse, I left. To this day, I don't really know the person who finally walked out, but I will always be grateful for that woman inside me who summoned the courage to leave.

My name is Nancy Salamone. I am going to tell you a story, and while it is a story of domestic violence, it is also a story of victory over violence.

For years, I kept a secret from my family and coworkers. I lived two lives. In one, I was a successful Wall Street executive; in the other, an abused wife. You'll notice I said family and coworkers, not friends, because I didn't have any. Why? Early on, my abusive husband isolated me.

Despite all the abuse I endured, there was a silver lining in my life— my career. Work was my safe haven. While I was abused at home, I thrived at the office. I was the go-to person, effective and energetic—the one who got things done. I rose to the position of vice president and was the only woman on our executive team.

I was fortunate to have a job that allowed me to determine my own travel schedule. I was the officer in charge of administrative activities for all the sales offices in the United States, and this required me to visit each office on a regular basis. I would travel three to five days a week, and yes, that enabled me to be away from my husband.

This story is a series of flashbacks. I cannot remember every incident—there are parts of my life with him that are buried deep within my psyche.

I do remember that the abuse started the day we got home from our honeymoon. It seems I didn't hang the bathroom towels correctly. After I was beaten and sexually assaulted that day, I lay on the bathroom floor, naked and bleeding. I was nineteen, and it was just the beginning of my marriage. The abuse—physical, sexual, emotional, and financial continued until I finally left twenty years later.

To understand how I allowed myself to be subjected to domestic violence for so long, I have to look back at my childhood. I was the eldest of three girls in a Sicilian, Roman Catholic family. My mother's family lived in our neighborhood in the Bronx, and since she was one of ten children, I had lots of aunts, uncles, and cousins. Family gatherings were frequently loud and boisterous, but I was told from a very young age that children should be seen and not heard, and I listened. I was not a loud or rambunctious child. If I was told to sit and be quiet, I did.

One day, when I was about five, my mom was altering one of my dresses. I was standing in front of the mirror and liked what I saw. I thought I was pretty. As I was standing there admiring myself, I said to Mom, "I'm beautiful."

My mom snapped back at me, "Never say that again. You sound conceited." I didn't know what conceited meant; after all, I was only five. The lesson I learned that day was that it was bad to feel good about myself.

My family lived with a code of silence known as omertà. To this day, generations of Sicilians still practice this code. It kept us from learning or talking about anything that would embarrass the family. Part of the reason I never told anyone about the abuse in my marriage was because of my Sicilian background, which instructed us to carry our cross in silence.

While I do not blame my family or my cultural background for the violence I experienced, my early years and upbringing did play a part, not only in how I got into a violent relationship, but also in why I stayed for so many years. The core values I was raised with made me yearn for a man who would take care of me, and I met that man as a teenager one summer day at Orchard Beach.

Orchard Beach was divided into numbered sections. The cool section for teens was 13, and that's where I was when he walked by with a girl on each arm. He was tall, dark, handsome, and I was instantly infatuated. Later that day, he left the two girls behind and approached me. He was a college guy, and I was a sophomore in high school. Imagine a college guy talking to me! He soon became my first and only boyfriend.

He was moody, and I naively thought I had the power to change his moods and make him happy. His moodiness would become worse, and he took his unhappiness out on me. But I stuck it out because I continued to think that I could fix him, as if I had some magical power. Of course, I was wrong.

Being from a good Catholic family and educated in a Catholic girls' school, I was indoctrinated with the belief that having sex before marriage was wrong. I was a teenager when we had sex, and I felt like a sinner. Even worse, I thought everyone knew what I had done. I felt like Hester Prynne in *The Scarlet Letter* with a big red "A" on my chest that everyone could see. I was scared and confused.

As the arguments escalated, I wasn't happy in the relationship, but I honestly thought that no other man would want me since I was no longer a virgin. I felt like tainted goods, so I stuck it out with him. When he finally asked me to marry him, it was with a sense of relief that I said yes. I wasn't in love; I was relieved. I married him when I was nineteen.

Looking back, I see that I was pushed into a life I didn't want, instead of following a vision of what I wanted my life to be.

One evening, after we'd been married for about two years, I went to the movies with my mother. As we were standing in line, I said, "Mom, I'm unhappy." Her reply was simple and direct: "You made your bed—lie in it." I never mentioned my unhappiness to anyone again. My mother didn't find out about the abuse until eighteen years later, when I finally left and showed up on her doorstep.

That day I had a moment of clarity like an out-of-body experience. He wasn't home and wouldn't be for a few hours. I saw myself packing a bag, walking out the door, and closing it behind me. I went to my mother's house, as I had no other place to go.

The first week I moved out, I did two things: First, I found a therapist; then I hired an attorney. For the first time in my life, I was on my own. I was scared to death of him and what he would do. I was thirty-nine and had never lived an independent day in my life.

Staying in an abusive relationship is dangerous, but leaving your abuser can be even riskier. Once I left, a new reign of terror began—not only against me, but against my coworkers, too. He constantly harassed us at work. He began to call my male counterparts and threatened to kill me, and them, too. I was terrified, so on the advice of my attorney, and now friend, Andrea, I hired a bodyguard.

Thankfully, I could afford protection. Many women in similar situations don't have the financial means to protect themselves. Unfortunately, there are tragic stories of how women who have left their abusers have been murdered by them.

After a few weeks of staying at my mother's house, my attorney told me she was informed that he had moved out of the apartment we shared. In fact, she was told he had moved out of New York. Given that piece of news, I let the bodyguard go and decided to move back into the apartment. Unfortunately, that was a bad decision.

On my second night back at the apartment, I heard the door open and there he was, in a rage. He moved quickly, grabbed me, and threw me against a closet door with such force that the door cracked. He picked me up, threw me on the couch, and got on top of me. He was screaming incoherently, and he started to choke me. As his hands continued to suffocate me, I closed my eyes and willed myself to relax. I thought, *Nance, this is it; you're going to die, so just relax. It'll be over soon.* I'd accepted that I was going to die and just wanted it to be as peaceful as possible. Perhaps because I didn't resist him, he suddenly stopped choking me and ran out of the house.

I sat on the corner of the sofa, not moving for a long time. Then, like a robot, I began to clean up the mess he had created. He'd thrown wine bottles, so I cleaned the walls and swept up the broken glass. When I was finished, I went to bed with a carving knife in my hand. I left all the houselights on, too. Thankfully, he didn't come back.

The next day, I went to work as usual. As I walked down the street to my office, a close associate and friend saw me and started calling my name. As he got closer, I could hear him say, "Nance, Nance. I had a dream about you last night. I dreamt you died." As he got closer, he said in a stunned voice, "What happened to your neck?" My neck was covered with welts and bruises, and like a journalist reporting the news, I was unemotional as I told him what had happened. I was basically numb and void of feelings that morning.

When I got to my office, I just sat there. I didn't answer the phone, open my mail, or even turn on the computer. I stared at the wall in front of me. A little while later, the same friend came into my office, urging me to call my therapist, but I couldn't move. I just looked at him and didn't say anything. I finally did contact my therapist and was later diagnosed with post-traumatic stress disorder. And, by the way, I never returned to that apartment again.

As I was going through my divorce, other executives and employees at the firm began to find out about the abuse I had endured during all the years they'd known me, and they rallied around me to keep me safe, even though they were harassed by my husband, too. None of them blamed me. In fact, the company I worked for came up with solutions to keep my coworkers and me safe. To this day, I wonder if they know how progressive they were.

Once my divorce was final and I was sure that he was gone, my new priority and fear related to money, and how I would manage my life. One day, during an intense budget meeting, it dawned on me that I made financial decisions every day to help further the goals of the corporation. I realized that I could bring that way of thinking into my personal life—more than just a way to handle money, I needed a way to use money to attain the life I wanted, a life I knew I deserved. As soon as the meeting was over, I went back to my office and labeled a folder "The Business of Me." That day, I began my journey to rid myself of the fears I had lived with for so many years, and I began to create a life built on personal and financial self-sufficiency.

As a final note, I will share with you that after my divorce I was finally living in my own apartment. One night I had a dream about a woman. She had the same hairstyle as I did, but I didn't see her face, as she was turned away from me. This woman walked up to a mirror and stopped in front of it. I saw her reflection. I was shocked—it was me, but it was not me. It was certainly my face and neck, but horribly scarred. I kept looking; I even put my hand up to touch the scars. But I wasn't afraid. In fact, I was fascinated and curious. I also didn't think the scars made me grotesque, even though they were shockingly ugly.

When I woke up the next morning, I was refreshed and at peace. To me, that dream meant that while I was emotionally scarred, I am a survivor. Finally free, I could move my life forward on my own terms.

For those of you who have endured abuse, know that there is help and you can leave and rebuild your life. You too can have Victory Over Violence.

National Domestic Violence Hotline 1-800-799-SAFE (7233)

The Historical Artist Goes Home

A story about Jasmine Germani

Jasmine Germani is a gemologist, designer, jeweler, geologist, scientist, artist, and publisher. She is also a proud daughter and mother—a woman of Sri Lanka, committed to celebrating and sharing the beauty and history of her homeland.

Jasmine studied in the field of scientific gemology, an ancient industry historically dominated by men. Gertrude Van Strackx was Ceylon's first female gemologist, and Ms. Van Strackx's secretary was Barbara Edirisinghe, who would go on to become the first chairperson of what was then called the Ceylon Gem Corporation. These women from the nineteen-seventies inspired a young, impressionable sixteen-year-old girl who a few years later, at nineteen, became one of the youngest members of the United Kingdom's gemological association.

Ms. Germani is a master of many disciplines; her broad intellectual interests and appreciation for unique experiences have led to her pushing boundaries in both the arts and sciences. Her genius is a sublime talent to craft heirloom-quality jewelry. The pieces she designs are aristocratic and mystical, with a touch of sculptural glamour. Royals, celebrities, and other affluent members of society have commissioned Jasmine's jewelry. Princess Diana, the Duke and Duchess of Wellington, and Nicole Kidman are some of the famous names associated with her dazzling creations. A unique diamond necklace was designed for Queen Noor of Jordan, in 1984.

It was a famed Sri Lankan blue sapphire that brought Jasmine her first sense of wonder at a young age. It was the starting point of a love affair that would take the free-spirited, fiercely independent young woman into the alluring world of gemstones and jewelry. All the while, she harbored ambitions to study medicine and become a doctor, following in the footsteps of her adored Cambridge-educated father, Dr. Gemunu Karunaratna.

The family lived in their majestic home, Gunfire, in Kandy, where Jasmine and her brother went to school. Jasmine actually being her middle name (Yasmine), her true first name is Avanti. Another ancestral property, the Monte Christo estate, was in Ratnapura. Avanti said, "It was here that I would develop a fascination for beautiful gems and jewelry."

When her grandmother, Murial Sri Nissanka, decided her high-spirited granddaughter with too much time to kill should become more serious about her life, she took her to meet her old friend, Gertrude Van Strackx. Jasmine was persuaded by Gertrude to do a correspondence course in gemology, to pass the time until she left to study medicine at University.

The changes in Sri Lanka, occurring in the seventies, began to affect Avanti's family, too. "Schools were closed for various reasons, leaving us with lots of free time. Since my brother Amal and I were protected by our eminent families, we were living an idyllic, carefree life." The gift of being born into affluence sheltered them from struggles many others had to endure.

Avanti's family was forced to move to New Zealand in April 1971, when an insurgency targeted her father and family in a life-changing event. The family left Sri Lanka in haste, with only a suitcase in each hand and without any money. Her father got a job in a hospital; however, the family had a hard time adjusting. To contribute, Avanti worked as a nurse's aide. Her first task was to learn to make hospital beds. "I still make beds hospital style," she laughs.

It was when her mother fell ill and money was scarce that the reality of their circumstances struck her. Tough times made her take stock of her affairs, and her future. After the carefree early years, this was a rude awakening, and it was during this time that Jasmine recollected her accordion teacher's caustic words—how she would always be a "jack-of-all-trades, master of none" because she didn't practice her lessons as a young girl. Those words haunted her.

"I told myself I would never be in second place. My parents had made a tremendous sacrifice, leaving behind a life of comfort to give us a chance at education.

"I realized to go after what I wanted, I had to aim for the stars. So, I decided to change my nonchalant attitude and master whatever I set out to do. I wanted to excel and at any cost." After Jasmine graduated with a major in geology from the University of Christchurch, the family moved to Adelaide, Australia, where she completed a medical science degree. Torn between medicine and gemology, she decided to pursue the latter at the Deutsche Gemological Institute in Germany. From there, she left for the United States, where she joined the Gemological Institute of America (GIA), in California, to complete her graduate studies.

Avanti became first Sri Lankan student to graduate from the GIA, topping her class in 1980. She was asked to teach at the GIA at a time when the founder, Richard T. Liddicote, was still teaching at the institute. Her destiny, though, lay elsewhere.

A fellow student, Michael Germani, from Italy, fell in love with the charismatic, stunning student from Sri Lanka. He pursued her relentlessly, won her over, and married her. Having earned their credentials in gemology, they both decided to go to the oil-rich kingdom of Saudi Arabia to explore new avenues for work. Avanti got a chance to work for the renowned billionaire, Robert Mouawad—jeweler to the Saudi King and the world's richest diamond owner. Jasmine would later go on to custom-make a jewelry collection for Elizabeth Taylor's perfume launch. A pair of blue sapphire and diamond earrings was given to Princess Diana. The sapphires were from Sri Lanka.

Avanti and Michael Germani became a power couple. An introduction to the eldest son and CEO of the Al-Rajhi Bank of Saudi Arabia, created another opportunity for the couple. The bank was looking to diversify into jewelry stores. Jasmine and Michael were offered the job of setting up the bank's jewelry stores for the Saudi market. Funded by the bank, the opening of five stores across the country gave them their first dream job.

"It was Arabian Nights come true. I had trays and trays of gems to play with," Avanti said of those days.

In their quest for perfect stones, they traversed the globe sourcing gems from Europe, Columbia, France, Brazil, Switzerland, Germany, Belgium, and Thailand, and bought sapphires from Sri Lanka. They visited Italy, the country that has for many years led trends in international jewelry designs. They made jewelry that captured the passions of men and women who love magnificent artwork.

Jasmine had her own personal collection of jewelry that she wore to parties and events. She began to specialize in restoration and redesigning of old jewelry, and she re-created bespoke pieces in homage to many famous personalities. The Saudi royal princesses would often get bored with their jewelry and would bring it to Avanti to have it redesigned.

When war broke out in the Middle East, in the early eighties, it was time to pack up and leave. Michael and Avanti relocated to Sydney, Australia where they went on to open four stores under their brand, Germani. Within a short period, the company had vertically integrated into design, manufacturing, and retail of high-end jewelry.

The clever and innovative marketing ideas behind the Germani brand, initiated by Jasmine, made the company one of Australia's coveted jewelry brands. The store became a household name when she got Germani involved as a sponsor for one of Australia's most popular TV series, called "The Sale of the Century." That alliance lasted fourteen years.

In 1990, Germani won the coveted De Beers Design Award for their diamond jewelry category and would go on to win the Australian Governor General's Award, twice in a row. As a member of Sydney's Powerhouse, a landmark science, design, technology, and decorative arts museum, Jasmine became part of a high-profile networked community. She also worked with numerous Australian charities. The company began to expand internationally, showcasing their jewelry in the United States, Europe, and Japan. A Germani boutique was also opened in Colorado, in the United States. They began to produce their own brand of perfume and accessories. The logistics to manage the international sales, though profitable, was tough. Now with a son and daughter to care for, the pressure was beginning to build.

"I was living my dream life; the one I had wanted since the age of sixteen. I was balancing a demanding job, was part of the elite, yet my concern was always to make sure my children, Tara and Amar, were well taken care of. Despite working, I drove my children to school, took them to their activities, and attended parent–teacher meetings."

The frantic pace of keeping up with home, family, and a high profile, international career eventually took a toll. Burnout was inevitable. Once again, despite a pattern of hard work and success, Avanti found herself at a crossroads. She had achieved the peak of each thing she set out to do, but had not yet found her own balance and inner peace. It occurred to her that regardless of family background or economic status, education and training, or personal dreams and aspirations, in time every woman must figure out who and what she wants to be.

To recuperate, she took a sabbatical year so she could return to her other love, art. She went to live in Italy and joined the famous Instituto Michelangelo. "I needed to give myself space to reflect and de-stress."

In 2009, when she was offered the chance to become a publisher in New York, her children were young adults, and she accepted. It was a challenge and a new adventure. New York is a tough city for fledgling publishers to break into.

Jasmine's first publishing effort was *Betrayal of Love and Freedom*, by New Zealand entrepreneur and author Paul Huljich, who cofounded Best Corporation (a pioneering organic foods company in New Zealand). A second book by the same author, *Stress Pandemic*, was also published by Avanti and went on to win four awards in the United States.

"I believe I am truly a renaissance woman. My efforts have never been about winning, but the fun in trying new things for the sheer experience."

Sitting in Central Park in New York City, one day Jasmine realized it was time to go home. She hadn't been back to Kandy, Sri Lanka in forty-two years. Kandy is where she spent her young life among loving family—aunts, uncles, and many cousins. "I was now older and hopefully wiser! What was I going to do after an exciting and adventurous life?"

One day a friend came by and asked what Jasmine was doing. She had just started to paint again. The friend had just opened a new hotel called Sandriana, on the same hill where Avanti lived all those years ago! The friend commissioned her to paint for his hotel, a challenge she embraced immediately. Her painting skills from art school in Florence, Italy, were about to be tested, on very large canvasses. "It was stimulating to be covered in paint. It was so far from the world I had left in fine jewelry for the rich and famous."

While attending a conference soon after this with her brother, they met a gentleman in the elevator who was attending the same program. They chatted with the man later on about the lecture, and when a stranger joined their conversation and asked Jasmine what she did for her occupation, she told him she was a historical artist. That man, Senaka Weeraratna, asked if she would be interested in painting the iconic architect, Devendra Mulachari, designer of a famous building in Kandy. He said it must be a celebration to show the great architect, a presentation of the masterpiece he had given to their beautiful land. "Sydney has the Opera House, and we have the Pathirippuwa," Jasmine explained.

After painting jewelry for forty years, Avanti's meticulous attention to detail impressed the high priest, who was pleased with her artwork. She wasn't sure at first if he was simply being kind and humoring her, but then he suggested that after the architect, Jasmine should paint another historical figure, the last Queen of Kandy. This was an ultimate compliment.

Since returning to her home, Gunfire, in Kandy, Jasmine is once again living in the land she claims is covered in gemstones—a gift of nature which took over four billion years to evolve. She has come full circle, back to the very place that laid the foundation for her calling in life. "It will be wonderful to be a part of leaving a legacy of our amazing, unbroken history of 2,300 years of this beautiful island—my homeland."

Monica & Me – A Story of Survival and Triumph

by Jean Messina

I am writing this story for and about my mother, Monica. Having an alcoholic mom who is also disabled had a powerful impact on my early life, and even now as an adult, our history has shaped me.

My mom dropped out of high school and left her home in Long Island to elope—mostly to get away from her abusive, alcoholic father. She ran off with a handsome navy man who was stationed in Maryland and gave birth to me on a navy base when she was seventeen years old. I was named Jean, after my grandmother. Unfortunately, my parents' marriage didn't last, and my mother and I came back to New York to live with my grandparents when I was still an infant. I saw my father only one time after that, when I was in my late twenties. He has never been a part of my life.

Monica liked to drink—a lot—and our lives changed forever on May 17, 1972, when I was four years old. She was walking across a busy road and was hit by a car. The near-fatal accident put her into a coma and left her with permanent brain damage, as well as other injuries like a broken jaw, damaged legs, and blindness in one eye. She spent six months in rehabilitation, learning to walk and talk again.

I don't remember what my mother was like before the accident, but I know it changed her as a person in many ways. Pictures from before show a stunning blond, with shoulder-length hair, bright blue eyes, and a petite frame. To this day, she loves to wear makeup and jewelry. I am the spitting image of her, and have heard all my life about how much we look alike.

When my mother came home from the hospital, she tried to be the best mother she could, but she couldn't do normal things that most moms do. She couldn't drive anymore, which meant we walked everywhere or took a cab. Sometimes my grandfather or grandmother would drive us places, but mostly we walked to school or into town, to the stores or church. Going to Disney World, camping, and other fun vacations were not an option for us. Our entire life was limited to one town.

We did spend a lot of time at her favorite hangouts, the local bars—drinking, smoking, and picking up anyone who would talk to her and give her attention. Like I said, Monica was beautiful, and she didn't have any trouble attracting men. With or without me, she spent many hours at the local bars. She would get drunk and attempt to walk home, many times falling down—bad balance from her injuries made worse by the alcohol. Cops frequently brought her home. After a while it became a regular thing and I treated it as normal. Most of the local police officers knew our family and were always nice to us. I think they felt sorry for her.

Some bars would tell Monica she couldn't come back for a while (they didn't want to get into trouble), and she would go to another bar to hang out. The bartenders liked my mother because she was sweet and pretty, and they felt sorry for her. I remember one bartender was especially kind. He always fed us and made sure that we got home safely by calling us a cab. He would always say to me, "Take care of your mommy, now."

As time went on, my mother drank more and more. She loved her beer, never liquor. My grandparents were also alcoholics, which made it easier for Monica to drink, and eventually my mother and grandmother became drinking buddies. Instead of helping her, they enabled her. Their destructive lifestyle was a constant source of embarrassment, hurt, and anger throughout my early years. I knew in my early teens, a time when you want to fit in rather than be different, that we were not normal. And on top of their drinking was the constant fighting. It was unbearable.

My grandfather loved drinking whiskey and gambling on horses. When he drank and lost a lot of money, he would get angry and violent, many times breaking things in the house and hitting my grandmother. He often left her with bruises, and she would cry all the time. I loved my grandmother. I spent a lot of time alone with her, especially in the evenings because my grandfather worked nights as a cook at a diner, and my mother was out at the bars.

My grandmother was what you would call a closet drinker. A victim of my grandfather's abuse, she tried to drink her pain away in private. In time, I learned why she drank so much "iced tea." It was because she put whiskey in it.

It was my grandmother who taught me how to put on makeup. We would spend nights watching old shows like *All in the Family* and *The Carol Burnett Show*, sitting on the couch while I put rollers in her hair. Sometimes she would cry and hug me, telling me she was sorry. I remember being very young, hugging her, and telling her that it was going to be okay.

My mother would come home late from the bars and climb into bed with me, smelling of alcohol, cigarettes, and urine from peeing in her pants. She did that a lot when she was drunk. She always told me that she loved me and asked if I loved her, too. I can still hear her voice and smell her like it was yesterday. I think some things never leave you.

Sometimes Monica would be mean to me and call me stupid because I wasn't doing well in school. When she was mad, she would grab my hair, digging her nails into my scalp so that I couldn't run away, and then hit me. I would scream for her to let go. For days it would hurt to brush my hair.

Whenever my mother walked me to school or came to pick me up in the afternoon, kids made fun of her, and that really hurt me. They called her retarded and stupid because she walked and talked funny. I guess since people didn't know about her accident and brain damage, they didn't understand.

My grandmother was the only one who ever went grocery shopping, but she was often too depressed to leave the house for weeks at a time, so there wasn't always food.

The big saying in our house was, "Don't tell strangers what's going on inside our home! It's no one's business." Sometimes, I would tell my teachers at school what it was like at home, even though I wasn't supposed to. Sometimes, it was evident what was going on without my saying anything.

On the night of my sixth-grade play, Monica left to go drink and came back completely intoxicated. She could barely walk, and I cried from embarrassment. The school called the cops and also the Department of Social Services. You can imagine how much I was stared at and made fun of after that. I didn't want to go back to school ever again.

Despite child protective services coming to our house on and off for years, it seems that I fell through the cracks of the system.

These memories leave my heart heavy, but there were some good times that Monica and I shared together. We went to church every Sunday and then walked up the block to the ice cream parlor for chocolate shakes. She loved to play bingo and I would go with her sometimes. Whenever my mother won money, she would get excited and happy, and we would go out to dinner with her winnings.

When I was younger there were some Easter holidays that were nice. My mother loved to put curlers in my long hair and put me in a pretty dress, bonnet, and cute shoes. I always got an Easter basket full of candy. Then we would go to church.

My mother loved going to church, praying to God, and talking to the priests (I could tell they loved and cared for her). They would always give her a special blessing, and I know that meant a lot to her. She tried to instill in me that religion and praying is important in life. I think she believed that God was the only one who could help her get better and take away her sadness. In spite of all the important parenting responsibilities she neglected, she made sure that I made my first communion and was confirmed, so I would be able to get married in a Catholic church. Even now, she still loves God and prays every day. I pray also, especially for her.

When my mother was first hit by the car and pronounced dead, then brought back to life, I wondered why God would do that to her—why He didn't take her, and instead, let her live with so much suffering. I was angry and stopped going to church because it never made sense to me how someone like Monica, who loved church and God so much, would be forced to endure such a hard life. I never saw God do anything to help her or me, and that made me mad. I remember lying in my bed at night, praying for my grandparents to stop fighting, praying for God to make my mother better, so that she could be like the other moms. I later realized that God could not help our family, and in my adult life, I went back to church to try and find my own peace.

My mother got an apartment near my grandparents' house; she wanted her independence. I think she wanted me to live with her, but I worried about leaving my grandmother alone with my grandfather. He had once been a wealthy businessman and talented artist. He had owned a stunning home and a boat because he loved to fish. I think that was his happiest time. He had been handsome in his day, but over time, alcohol stole his good looks and beautiful wife, and his temper lost him his children. Eventually, he lost everything until he was selling anything he could to pay off debts. When he couldn't keep up, the violent rages would punish us all.

I stayed with my mother almost every weekend and went back to my grandparents' house on Sunday nights. When I was fifteen, my grandparents sold the house and made plans to move to Georgia, to be near my grandfather's sister. They put my clothes in black garbage bags and made me leave with a woman my grandfather knew from work, telling me that they would come to say goodbye before they left to go south.

Why did they leave and never say goodbye? Why didn't they take me with them? Didn't they love me? Wasn't I worth taking? It all happened quickly. Why didn't I go live with my mother? I can't say. She apparently didn't want me either. Was I just a burden to everyone?

Needless to say, at fifteen, I was angry and sad; I felt worthless and unloved. It left me coping with abandonment issues that affected me for many years. I started to drink and smoke, and I hung out with other kids who were on a dangerous path. Because I had no family, my friends became my family, and I did have many good times over the years.

In time, the people I was living with didn't want to deal with me anymore. They were supposedly there to help troubled teens, but again I wasn't wanted. They also packed up the few belongings I had and took me back to live with my mother in her tiny apartment. I was turning sixteen, and now it was just the two of us.

Monica didn't give me the key to the apartment because she said she didn't trust me. I became an angry teenager and spent my time partying and trying to get through high school. Monica often had men in and out of the apartment, or some nights she wouldn't come home at all. I would sleep at a friend's house, in the local park, or sometimes in the lobby of our building when she didn't come home. When she did reappear, we fought. She was always drunk and I was always furious with her.

Eventually I met Margaret, a young girl who lived in the same building. Margaret and her mom let me into their lives and eventually took me in. That helped me get through a tough time, and they became my new family. Margaret became the sister I'd never had. We are both only children and we adopted each other. It meant so much to me to have her and her mom accept me. If it wasn't for them, I don't know what would have happened to me.

In time, they moved out of the building into a house, and I wound up spending a lot of time there, living with them more steadily than I ever had anywhere else. It was a spring day in 1985 when I went to my mother's apartment to get some of my things and found that everything was gone—our furniture, most of my clothes, and my mother—gone! My uncle had packed our stuff and put Monica on a bus to go live with my grandparents in Georgia. I remember yet again feeling hurt and confused that she had left me behind without a word, but looking back now, I don't think she could handle living on her own. Between her drinking and her injuries, it was too hard for her. She needed my grandmother because I had left when living with her had become too hard for me.

I stayed in New York with Margaret and her mom. Because I was only sixteen, I was considered abandoned and neglected, and I was in custody of the Department of Social Services until I turned eighteen. Funny how that worked out, since they never helped me when I was younger.

If it hadn't been for the school social worker and a special education teacher who cared about me, I don't know if I ever would have made it through high school. Yes, I actually graduated. It meant a lot to me to wear that cap and gown. Unfortunately, my mother wasn't there, though I thought about her all that day.

In her defense, Monica didn't completely abandon me. She wrote letters and sent cards for years. I still have them, all wrapped up in ribbon. At least I knew she was thinking of me.

After high school, my boyfriend went off to college, and I hung out with new friends but felt terrible. Most people my age were going to college, traveling, dating and having fun—enjoying life. Back in high school, hard as it had been, there was a place to go every day where I felt safe. Teachers, friends, and especially my social worker were all welcoming faces in the Monday-to-Friday routine. I actually believed they cared about me. Once that was all gone, I didn't know who I was. I knew only that everyone who was supposed to love me had left me without a word. I was partying more than ever, but it wasn't a party. Again, I was lost and alone.

One night I took a bottle of pills and drank a lot of alcohol. I hoped to fall asleep and not wake up. I didn't want to feel bad anymore. That led to my first experience in a hospital psychiatric ward. Throughout my twenties I was in and out of the hospital for anxiety and depression. Most of that decade is a blur. I was diagnosed and labeled with various kinds of mental illness, on all kinds of psychiatric medication, sometimes too much, and I got addicted to tranquilizers.

When you sink that low, the hospital becomes a safe place. Sometimes I would even pretend that I was suicidal again, just so that I could go back in. People in my life couldn't deal with me anymore. I lost relationships with guys and friends. I lost good jobs and a decent place to live. In time, I think I got used to institutional life. I felt that I actually belonged somewhere. I know it sounds weird, but I couldn't make sense of what I was going through. I wanted only to feel safe and welcome.

It was difficult to work my way out of depression when I was constantly overmedicated. I didn't believe I would go to college or do anything important. I certainly wasn't going to get married or have a family of my own. What man would want to be with me?

Eventually, I was living with someone I truly cared about, and I thought that we might have a chance for a future together. But then my grandparents died only a few months apart, and that changed me again. With help from friends, I bought the cheapest airfare we could find, and I went to Georgia to say a final goodbye. In a rundown trailer park home that was dirty and depressing, my grandparents had literally drunk themselves to death. Their years of suffering from alcoholism and depression were over, and I hoped they were finally at peace together. Unfortunately, Monica was an absolute mess from watching her parents die in front of her and from years of her own self-destructive behavior. She had to go into the hospital for the help she needed. I couldn't help her.

I will never forget the day I had to leave my mother by herself in Georgia. The guilt and sadness I felt was overwhelming, and it went on for years. When I came home from Georgia, I had a breakdown. I had panic attacks. I didn't want to leave the apartment. I went back into the hospital voluntarily, and my fiancé stopped visiting me. He told me that our relationship was over. Talk about hitting rock bottom. I wanted to give up, but I had to start over.

The social worker found an apartment for me to share with a woman, in a building where other people with mental illness lived. I still had a few friends who helped me along the way, but I had to be in therapy and go to a day program. I had to take my medication. I had to abide by all the rules, or I would be homeless. I had no control over my life and spent a lot of time in my bedroom alone. Out my bedroom window, I could see the backyard of the house next door. I would watch the couple that lived there with their two children and would get so sad wishing that was me. Somehow, I had to make peace with myself—that was not the life I was meant to live.

I didn't want to watch other people and feel jealous anymore. I had to fight to get out of the system and earn a decent life for myself. It felt like I was screaming and no one was hearing me. I was angry at the world and at everyone who had hurt and abandoned me. And I was sick and tired of being sick and tired.

In time, I moved into another apartment, and found a great therapist. She was amazing, seemed to really understand me, and helped me to realize that it was up to me. I had more power over my circumstances than I thought. I couldn't give up or be self-destructive anymore. I had to keep positive and focus on goals for the future. I eventually stopped taking all medications; it was important not to depend on medicine to be strong. I needed to learn to deal with my feelings without antidepressants and antianxiety pills.

I was cleaning houses and making good money, and starting to feel good about myself.

I met a guy and we started dating, but our relationship went south when he returned to a life of drug use. I did not want to go down that road again. I decided to leave him. For the very first time, I felt some self-worth. This time when I moved on, I wasn't alone. I had Margaret and her husband and other friends supporting me. I went to live with Margaret and her husband, and I got a new job.

During this transition, my good friend Lou was there for me. He'd known me since I was seventeen—he knew about my family and my past, everything I had been through. While I was living with Margaret, Lou and I became closer. He helped me realize that I am a good person, and he wanted to spend time with me. I always had fun with him; he made me smile. Our friendship grew stronger until eventually things got romantic between us. By this time I was a completely different person. I was stronger emotionally than I had ever been, and I had confidence in myself for the first time ever.

We fell completely in love and wound up living together. I became a part of his wonderful, fun-loving Italian family who took me in and accepted me unconditionally. I adored his mother. She was the most loving, kind, fun person, and she loved and treated me just like one of her own daughters. She became the mother I had never had. That meant the world to me. The day came when he asked me to marry him. It was the happiest and most exciting day ever!

As we planned our wedding, feelings came up about my mother. She wouldn't be able to help me plan and do all the fun things mothers do to help their daughters plan weddings. Of course it made me sad. I hadn't seen her since my grandparents had died, and felt the need to see her in order to get married and be happy. I had to forgive her and make peace with the past, so that I could truly move on. There was a part of my life that still needed to be healed, and Lou agreed that we should go visit Monica.

We went to see her a month before our wedding. I remember saying to Lou, "This is the first time in my life that I am spending time with my mother and she isn't drunk." As we prepared to leave and go back to New York, pain and guilt overwhelmed me. I cried all the way to the airport; it broke my heart to leave her alone again. I knew I had to take care of myself, but at this point I was older, stronger, healthier, and she was sober. This time was different. I wanted to help.

She wasn't the greatest mother to me. I know that! But after years of counseling and learning about myself, I had learned to forgive. As we left, I came to realize that my mother had lived a sad, tough life that in some ways was maybe even harder than mine had been. It wasn't all her fault. She had suffered from the illness of alcoholism and had never gotten the help she needed because her own parents were so sick and unable to help her.

My special day came on September 24, 2005. I got married! I wore a beautiful wedding dress that my mother-in-law helped me pick out. We got married in a church. All of our friends and family were there to help us celebrate. Margaret was my maid of honor. It was perfect, and I was truly happy.

We went back to see my mother again in the spring of 2006, and in September we brought her home to New York. I know some people didn't understand why I was doing it, but it was something I needed to do, for Monica and for me. I could not turn my back on her. I don't turn my back on people I love. Maybe it's because so many people did it to me, but I was a strong woman, with a full, happy life, and I wasn't going to let her bring me down anymore. I was going to be there for her.

In February 2007, I found out that I was going to become a mother. I was so happy, but scared. I didn't have a good role model. I had no idea how to be a good mother.

When I told Monica about the pregnancy, she was excited to be a grandmother. She told everyone in the nursing home she couldn't wait. My mother, who wasn't even there when I graduated high school or when I got married, would be present and sober to meet her grandchild.

On October 31, 2007, I delivered a healthy baby boy. It was the second happiest day of my life, and my mother was there to hold her grandson. It meant so much to both of us. I am a mother and a wife and a daughter.

I guess my therapist was right—I am here for a reason. My son is now nine years old, and he is the happiest boy, full of life and love. Not a day goes by that I don't make sure he feels loved, special, important, and wanted. I want more than anything to be the mother to him that I never had. Love is like food or oxygen. Everyone needs it.

Lou and I became foster parents with the hope of helping other children who aren't getting the love and care they deserve. We fostered one young boy for a year, and then he went back to his parents, and we were happy for him. We still keep in touch with him and see him once in a while. He and our son are good friends.

Sure, there are days that I go to bed feeling a little less than confident in my parenting skills, but I know that my son feels my love every single day, and he tells me every day that he loves me to the moon and back, and that I am beautiful. I can't even put into words what it feels like when he looks at me and says that.

My husband and I try our best to be good parents. We are raising him to be a kind, thoughtful person. We've taken him to Disney World and gone on family trips that I could never have even imagined when I was a kid. It's like reliving my childhood through him, and that is a gift beyond measure. My son has taught me what it's like to be a happy child, to be silly and have fun. I believe he will grow up to be a confident person who will take on the world.

Margaret and I remain sisters to this day. Her daughter and my son are growing up together, seeing each other on holidays and birthdays, sharing the happy occasions and celebrations of childhood.

As for Monica, she is in a nursing home only fifteen minutes away from me, and I go and spend time with her a few days a week. As time moves on, she is slowly disappearing because of dementia. I can no longer take her out to dinner or to church. She can no longer walk and do things on her own. It saddens me every time I see her, but I know she's not alone. She is safe and being taken care of, and someday God will take her home to be with my grandparents again. I hope she will be at peace.

I believe in angels and know that certain people were put into my life for a reason. Whether it was a teacher, a social worker, or a therapist who told me that I must not give up, or friends who never gave up on me, I'm grateful.

Maybe I'm here to be an angel for my mother or my son, or someone I haven't met yet. What I know for sure is that I am a survivor. I am loved, and I am important. Through all the highs and lows, I have emerged a better woman, not only for myself, but also for my family and for everyone I hold in my heart.

I am reminded of a favorite quote from the Dalai Lama: "Love and compassion are necessities, not luxuries. Without them, humanity cannot survive."

Lion Lullabies

by Shanna Sussens

When I turned thirty, I was exactly where I had hoped to be at that point in my life. I was starting a career as a travel agent, which was exciting and seemed perfect for me because I love to travel and immerse myself in new cultures.

My fat cat and I lived together in a beautiful old stone house with a creek in the backyard. I was within walking distance of anywhere I needed to go in town. For the first time in my life, I bought a car because I wanted it, not because I was desperate to find a new one before my old car died. I was totally independent. This is what life at thirty is supposed to be like, right?

I was content living alone, but life wasn't without challenges. I tried (unsuccessfully) to get my cat to eat spiders because I am terrified of them and there wasn't anyone around to get rid of them for me. He ate cobwebs and other insects, so why couldn't he eat spiders?

It was often dark when I left for work and dark when I got back home. My normal two-hour commute was sometimes extended to five or six hours when winter snowstorms hit. I was too exhausted to do anything after a workday, and with almost all of my money going toward bills, I was growing bitter about living to work, itching for adventure and something new—something meaningful.

I saved my vacation and sick days to take a proper vacation. My plan was to visit a friend in South Africa and do a road trip through Kruger National Park. This would surely ease my restlessness, at least for a while.

South Africa was an adventure I had longed for since I was young. As an animal lover, it was a dream of mine to go on safari. In my early twenties, I worked for Disney and had the chance to visit their Animal Kingdom theme park. At the time, I had believed that was the closest I would get to an authentic safari experience, so you can only imagine my joy when I got the opportunity to see the real thing.

The trip was amazing. I fell in love with South Africa on my first morning there. After ten days, I said a tearful goodbye, but I knew I'd visit again. When I returned home and resumed my routine, I found I was no longer happy. There was simply no way that could be it for my life. How could I sit behind a desk all day, trying to convince people to spend their savings on whatever vacation package I was told to push? Was that really how I wanted to spend the bulk of my time?

It wasn't long before I decided to quit my job and return to South Africa to spend a few weeks volunteering for the nonprofit organization Pride 'n Purpose (PnP). PnP is the charitable arm of Ulusaba Private Game Reserve, in the Greater Kruger National Park. The organization focuses on improving the lives of the impoverished communities just outside the reserve's border. I had no plan other than to enjoy my time and do something I could be proud of. My family was always supportive of my adventures, so if all else failed, I would be a broke, thirtysomething living with my parents when I came back home. Not exactly something to look forward to, but I was too excited about returning to South Africa to worry about what might follow.

The doubts came during my typical night-before-the-flight panic. Was I crazy? Could I really move to the African bush where lions and leopards might roam into our camp? I couldn't even take care of the spiders in my house—how was I going to survive lions? I didn't know which insects could kill me. Was my new home going to be full of them? Would I wake up with a giant hairy spider on my face?! Maybe I should have opted for the malaria tablets. I had only just started making it on my own in small-town America. Was it selfish to leave my family (and cat) only to rely on them again when I'd have to start all over?

My mind was full of conflicting thoughts—current worries and possible future regrets. *I should have been better to my mom. I should have spoiled my fat cat more. It's only a few weeks; I'll be happy I took this leap. When I'm an old lady, I want to look back on my life and be proud. Do I really want my life to be shaped by society's expectations? Or do I want to step outside the lines to find adventure and real happiness? This is my only life; I'm going for it.*

My fat cat moved in with my parents, and I was off.

After a grueling thirty-plus hours of traveling, I settled into the relaxed social atmosphere of Ulusaba. I lived in the staff village with the rest of the Ulusaba and PnP employees. We were pretty deep in the bush; it was a forty-minute drive to the gate to leave the reserve, then twenty minutes on dirt roads through the villages, and another thirty minutes on the tar road before reaching the nearest town. A night out for beer and pizza required a half day off of work. Getting to a bigger town, one with a mall and movie theatre, was a six-hour round-trip drive. We were isolated but had everything we needed. We had modern comforts like air conditioners, washing machines, and Wi-Fi. However, many things made this very different from home. Our roofs were thatched (made of grass). Wi-Fi and power weren't reliable. I learned to complete my shower routine in the dark, and had to convince my family that it didn't mean I was dead if they didn't hear from me for a few days.

The staff village consisted of about one hundred people living in homes surrounded by an electric fence—meaning that wild animals were literally surrounding us. We were living on their turf in the middle of the bush, and the electric fence gave a false sense of security—if an elephant wanted in, he would get in (I know this from experience). Checking my shoes for scorpions and looking under my pillow for spiders was now part of my daily routine. When an elephant would sneak in to steal some marula fruit, we would get out of bed to watch him helping himself to our fruit trees, in awe of him and frightened of his size. Leopards were in and out of camp, sometimes even under the house I slept in.

Being isolated created a tight-knit community. Everyone welcomed me, taught me the local lingo, introduced me to braais (barbeques), and showed me which creatures to steer clear of. Working in the bush for six weeks straight, everyone was used to making their own fun. There were theme parties for every occasion, braais every few days, and staff game drives whenever possible. One night after a few games of pool and too many drinks, my pool teammate (a park ranger), Matthew "expelliarmused" a cupcake right out of my hands. That struck a chord with my inner Harry Potter dork, and he has kept my attention ever since. We became good friends, and eventually even more.

I spent my days helping to set up PnP's tenth preschool, Ekurhuleni. I worked with the amazing ladies who volunteer as teachers there—we painted, set up classrooms, and got to know the sweet children. At first, the little ones were in tears if I came too close. Most of them hadn't seen or interacted with white people unless it was a doctor pricking them for shots. But after a few weeks, they came running to the *bakkie* (pickup) as soon as I arrived and showered me with hugs and love. Their acceptance and affection meant a lot to me. It made me feel like I was doing something worthwhile.

Ekurhuleni started with twenty-five kids in a small dark building that was on the verge of crumbling. I got there just as construction of the new building finished. (In fact, their old school did fall to the ground after a particularly bad storm, though luckily, no one was hurt.) The new school had long-drop toilets, a jungle gym, a kitchen, and eventually, a vegetable garden.

By the time we finished setting everything up, there were over sixty children attending. It was amazing to see the transformation of this school and the teachers' pride in it. I could see the difference we were making. About fifteen years earlier, before PnP was around, most children in the local communities didn't go to school until they were eight years old. The government didn't assist with preschools, and there was no other option.

The preschool's fees are only sixty rand a month, which is just under five US dollars. This includes five days a week at the school and two meals per day. Some of the kids aren't able to have a healthy meal at home, so the program ensures that they can get some of the vitamins and nutrients they need while they are in school.

With Ekurhuleni looking and doing great, I started to upgrade the classrooms of other schools. I assisted with taking Ulusaba guests on tours, showing them how much need is just outside of their five-star lodge. I got to speak with guests from all over the world and helped to spark their interest in our work.

It wasn't difficult for guests to realize how privileged they were—even the children could see this. One visiting boy, about eight years old, met a boy his age who was barefoot with tattered clothing. Before leaving, the young visitor took off his own shoes and gave them to this boy.

I had a lot of time to reflect and focus on learning new things, and I enjoyed it. I started learning Portuguese, read a ton of books, and learned about the wildlife. For the first time, I experienced racism and learned about the major problems South Africa and surrounding countries face and the distressing issues people deal with every day. I saw first-hand how people can be brushed aside and forgotten while they struggle to meet basic human needs. I got to know people with heartbreaking stories of survival—some without happy endings.

There was also time to enjoy the beautiful wildlife and scenery. Matthew shared his extensive knowledge of the bush and local wildlife. We started meeting for lunches, movies, and working out together, always accompanied by his awful jokes, which I loved. He always motivated me to do my best and never made me feel like an outsider, even though I was.

I joined as many game drives as I could and never tired of going out into the bush. Staff would meet in front of our offices with a beautiful view of the sun setting over the Drakensberg Mountains. Matt and I went on holiday together where he introduced me to Ntombi, one of the cheetahs he and his family have raised since her mother, a rescued cheetah, was killed by a lion. What would be an ordinary, lazy afternoon at home in the States was incredible here, napping under a Baobab tree that was nearly two thousand years old with the Drakensberg as a backdrop.

My "couple of weeks" quickly turned into three months, which turned into six months. I was loving my new lifestyle. When the six months were coming to an end, I began to worry. There was no way I could go back to a meaningless desk job. I'd be thirty-two, living with my parents, and probably jobless for at least a few months. I held on to the hope that maybe I could find another job I'd be passionate about, but deep down I knew I'd have to take any job in order to get by. Matthew and I were close now, but we both knew my departure was coming and refused to deal with it.

Then came good news. The PnP administrator was leaving, and they asked me to temporarily fill in for her during her absence! Perfect! Ten more months to delay my dreaded return to the "real world."

I was ready to take on the administrative responsibilities and make the most of my newly extended time. This was not like any office I'd ever seen before. The doors and lounge were open to the bush, allowing for some cool sightings. We regularly had warthogs, vervet monkeys, and various antelope passing through. Occasionally, we had more dangerous visitors like night adders and scorpions. One evening, we were stuck late in the office when a few elephants came to snack on the trees just outside our door.

I learned my new role as I went, and after a couple months we had everything running smoothly. Procedures were in place, new projects were happening, and donations were coming in. I couldn't have been happier. This was an opportunity to do good, help others, and show the skeptics that one hundred percent of our donations go into our projects, not our pockets.

My volunteer stipend barely got me by, but I didn't need much. I learned to live a simple life, my values shifting away from the material things that used to seem important. Matthew and I became experts at living comfortably on a tight budget, still finding ways to have fun. We spent most of our time in the bush rather than rushing back to civilization. We took countless trips into Kruger, and we spent a lot of time between his family's two lodges.

The lodge his grandmother started, Tshukudu, is a place like no other. They take in rescued animals, so there are special opportunities to have close encounters with rare wildlife. We'd often see cheetahs lounging by the pool near guests sunbathing and children running around. We'd make special visits to see Bhecki, the elephant that was orphaned during a culling and raised there on the reserve. Bhecki loves getting treats from us—apples, bananas, and marulas. Farazi, a hippo, was relocated from a zoo in Switzerland and likes to snuggle up by the fire on winter nights. Quite a few guests cook their dinner over the fire and get the fright of their lives when Farazi walks over.

Whether in Tshukudu, Ulusaba, or Kruger, every drive into the bush was unique and fascinating. Watching such beautiful creatures in their natural habitat rather than in cages at a zoo was incredible.

By now, my old life seemed terribly far away, and it was so much more than the physical distance. I had adventure in my life and purpose in my work. The extraordinary was becoming my ordinary. PnP had accomplished amazing things since I had arrived. We built our first-ever flushing toilets for a school, funded a primary school's eco club field trip into Kruger Park, completed our eleventh preschool, provided laptops and two years of Wi-Fi for a primary school, and celebrated the tenth anniversary of a local clinic by supporting a company that provides free hearing aids and testing.

My ten months were coming to an end, and again, I was getting anxious about returning to meaningless work. Luckily, once again I got last minute good news. They asked me to stay, permanently! We quickly found an agent and did all we could to ensure a work visa, but there was nothing more we could do but wait . . . two years, to be exact.

While hoping to extend my volunteer visa, I spent months back in the States, not knowing if or when I would see Matthew again. I didn't know if I would return to the bush or what would happen to PnP with only one employee left on site. Returning to live in the United States felt like giving up on both Matthew and PnP. I continued to work for the organization from home, but my South African volunteer stipend was nowhere near enough to get me by (it takes 14 South African rand to equal 1 US dollar). I tried to remain hopeful that my extension would come through, but I was constantly debating how long I could live like this and when I would have to give up.

It took a little time to readjust to life back home, where things were fast-paced and everything you could want is readily available. I had forgotten how many choices of cereal (or anything else) are in US supermarkets compared to PnP's usual two or three options. And fresh milk—I won't ever take that for granted again! When I heard a police siren, I perked up, initially mistaking it for a hyena call. I could go for a run without worrying about ending up as dinner for a big cat. I realized how many people (including myself) take water for granted; not like in the bush, where every rainfall is precious and celebrated. Pennsylvania spiders don't come close to instilling the kind of fear that a baboon spider or red roman causes (Google them—they are nightmares brought to life).

Matthew came to visit me twice, and each time, we had to say goodbye without knowing if it would be our last. I was still waiting for my extended visa to be approved, and my heart couldn't handle it. He had become a major part of my life, and was becoming my family. I couldn't imagine life without him. That was a long, dark time for me. Without the work visa, I would have to keep living on the volunteer stipend instead of a proper salary. How could Matthew and I move forward when I could barely support myself? I was constantly thinking about our future and about my family. If there were an emergency, it would break my bank account to get back to either location. I could not afford to live a life split over two continents earning a volunteer's income.

The bush had become my home. It's comforting to fall asleep to hundreds of frogs croaking and lions or hyenas calling. I woke excited to see what each day would bring. My new routine was to go with the flow because you never know what will happen in the bush. Taking time to appreciate the beauty around me was a welcome change and not something I wanted to give up. When a praying mantis crawled out of my hair, I didn't even flinch. (But I will never be okay with the giant spiders.)

When my visa extension finally came through, I swore I would never go through that again. We would have to find a better way to make this work.

One especially beautiful afternoon, we took a break from the stress of big decisions and went for a drive in the bush. We found Bhecki and her family, who came running to greet us, as we had brought marulas for them. The sun was setting with beautiful hues of reds and oranges while the young elephants were having a blast, trumpeting and chasing each other through tall grass—a powerful reminder of what we were struggling for. Suddenly, Matthew dropped to one knee and proposed.

I never realized how much love and happiness I could experience by following my heart. I don't know exactly what new adventures are in store for us, but I do know that I will never settle for an unfulfilling life.

Tough Girls Wear Anchors

by Maurine Conrad

*Please note that this story contains a description of sexual assault.

When you believe you are unworthy of love, when you have been told you were not wanted, there is an undeniable loneliness that lies deep within your heart. To protect yourself, you don't let anyone into that space because there is room only for your pain. That pain belongs to you, and you are not sharing it. You put up a façade that you are a strong girl, a tough girl, but sometimes that is not enough. So you run. Run far away.

At seventeen, in the mid-seventies, I joined the navy. Why? Because sometimes you just have to try and love yourself.

Now I am a woman—a proud Native American woman, a daughter, a wife, a mother, a grandmother, a United States Navy sailor, and an advocate for the protection of Native American rights and veterans' rights and benefits.

I am a member of the Karuk Tribe—people who were nearly decimated during the California gold rush, who lived during the time of tribal terminations, and who sometimes tried to hide that they were native in order to live and maybe succeed in a white world; people who were denied the right to know their language and traditional ways, whose children were taken away and placed in boarding schools to learn how to become "decent human beings." What kind of shit is that, right? They say the traumas of past generations live on; I think that is true.

My father was a navy man, and he was always gone. It was so exciting when he came home from deployment because I knew he would have a gift for me from the faraway places he had been. He was so very proud of his service to his country, so maybe that is why I chose the navy. I knew that my life would probably go nowhere if I didn't leave. I didn't want to end up pregnant and become a drunk or a drug addict like some of my family members—I wanted a reason to love myself, to be proud.

Because I was only seventeen, my mom had to go with me to the recruiter's office. We talked, and then I had to fill out all the paperwork. Right away, I was stumped on how to answer what my race was, so I asked my mom if I should put Native American. She said, "No! I want you to have a chance to succeed. If you put Native American you may not get the opportunities you deserve. Mark it Caucasian." So there you go, I had to hide that I was a Native American. I marked it Caucasian and finished the application.

The recruiter let us know that I would be scheduled for aptitude and ability testing, and that I would have to go to Oakland for a physical. I was entering on a delayed-entry program (because of my young age) and scheduled to take my oath of enlistment in January. I would then head to Orlando for boot camp. I was disappointed that I had to wait, but at the same time, I was thrilled that in six months I'd be on a journey that would hopefully change my life for the better.

I found myself flying across the United States for the first time. Boot camp was a blur of standing in ranks, marching, cleaning, getting yelled at, physical training, getting rubella, and spending a week in bed, sicker than I had ever been before. Inspections, more getting yelled at, lots of girls crying, and then it was over.

I received orders to go to Bainbridge, Maryland for training. I was going to work in communications. There were fewer restrictions on us at the training center, but this was my introduction to the challenges I was going to face being a woman in the military. I received orders to go to Guam—thinking, where the eff is that? I had to have an overseas screening, I guess to find out if I had any medical or other issues that might prevent me from serving there. I was told to report to Warrant Officer So-and-so's office for my interview. When I got there, he was sitting with his feet up on the desk and a cup of coffee in his hand, giving me the once-over. He asked some general questions, and then: "Do you know why you are going to Guam?"

I replied with a big smile on my face. "Yes sir. I am going to be a radioman."

"Don't you know what's going on in the world, girl? You are going there for the morale of the men."

Talk about being thrown back into the house of pain that I had worked so hard to run from. There was more of this from the men I served with in Guam. I was the only woman in my work center, and I got what I now know was the usual hazing of the newbie. But there were also sexual innuendos, followed by bold statements that if I wanted a good evaluation or promotion I needed to put out. I did my best to ignore it all. Like many women in service, I didn't say or report anything. Doing so would result in more of the same or worse. When I suffered a physical assault, I was thankful it hadn't been sexual, even though I believe that was where it had been headed. I covered my bruises and went on. My self-worth continued to decline, which led to a lot of drinking and partying.

That warrant officer back in Bainbridge was somewhat right—Guam was one of several R&R spots for soldiers and sailors during the Vietnam war. We monitored the communications coming out of the American embassy when Saigon fell and the embassy was overrun—there was screaming and gunfire coming through those radios. Shortly after, a bunch of us were taken down to the naval base to work in Tent City, where Vietnamese evacuees coming into Guam by ships and planes were processed for entry into the United States. I worked eight hours on, eight hours off for about a week in the baby tent, where we ensured that babies were diapered before their parents went through processing. We also provided formula, baby food, and blankets for the babies and sanitary napkins for their mothers.

The older Vietnamese men and women would come to our tent crying and begging for food and blankets. One mother ran into the tent holding a limp baby whom she immediately placed in my arms. The mother was sobbing, and all the while saying something I didn't understand. What I did understand was that the baby was in bad shape, and I think the woman believed we were doctors. I ran to the medical tent, but it was too late, the infant had died in my arms. My heart was broken, and the door to my room of pain was reopened.

When I look back at this, I am amazed that as a young woman—a girl, really—I dealt with all of this in such a short period of time. I was broken, but I went on. Sometimes you just have to try and love yourself.

Fast-forward through two failed marriages and two children, more duty stations and more sexual harassment, more trying to prove to the men that I was a great sailor and that I could do the job. I was still feeling bruised, like I wasn't worth anything more than what was between my legs. I kept wishing I could just be me, just be accepted, damn it!

One in six women in the service suffer some form of sexual trauma; it occurs more frequently in the army, navy, and marine corps. I was thankful again that my previous physical assault had not been sexual, and promised myself that I would never allow physical violence to happen to me again—I would not be that one in six.

Then it happened.

I had been in the navy for about thirteen years. Things were still difficult as far as sexual harassment was concerned, but I had learned to deal with it. It was their problem, not mine. I was advancing on schedule and had finally been selected for the elite rank of chief petty officer.

It was a beautiful Saturday on a remote island in the Indian Ocean. There was going to be a big barbecue and beach party after we got off work. There was great food, volleyball, music, dancing, swimming, and a lot of alcohol. It was a good time, but I had way too much to drink. The party was still in full swing when evening came. I went to find a bathroom and was thinking maybe it was time for me to head back to my barracks. I was a bit wobbly walking along and not entirely sure where I was because it was so dark. The next thing I knew I was knocked to the ground—or did I fall? No, there was someone on top of me! *Do I scream? No, I can't—my face is being smashed into the ground. Oh my God, what is happening? Who is that? I can't see!*

He flipped me over, and I started to scream, and he hit me in the face and growled at me to shut up. I didn't recognize the voice, didn't know what to do. He was strong and trying to rip my clothes off. I was trying to fight, but he was big, and he was heavy. He hit me again and again. I peed on myself, and he got mad and started dragging me somewhere. I reached for anything I could grab onto, but there was nothing. I screamed again and he kicked me.

I started to figure out that if I didn't want to get hit or kicked, I'd better not scream. I thought, *Just rape me already if that's what you're going to do, then maybe you'll let me go.* I couldn't fight. I couldn't think straight. I just wanted it to stop.

The next thing I knew, he was picking me up and pushing me through a window or something like that. I fell, and he was on me again. He tried to enter me. I was hitting him and bit his arm. He flipped me over and entered me from behind. My mind was gone. I couldn't fight him. *Please, please stop!* I was crying. I couldn't comprehend what was happening.

He flipped me over again and entered me. I hurt so badly! I think I passed out for a while. Then I was alone and scared. *Is he still here? Is he watching me?* I lay still and waited, listening. I don't know for how long. Finally I sat up, *Oh God, I hurt!*

I had to get to my room. *Where am I?* I felt around and found my clothes and put them on. It was so dark. I found a window and climbed through it, falling to the ground. I saw a little bit of light shining. *Do I want to go that way? What if someone sees me?* So I went in the opposite direction. When I got to the end of the building, I saw more light, and I huddled there, trying to make sure no one else was around. I finally recognized where I was and made my way to my barracks. Thank God I didn't see anyone. I got into my room, locked the door, and pulled the drapes closed. I fell on my bed and cried myself to sleep.

When I woke later, every inch of my body hurt. My cheek, eye, and side were bruised, and I had scrape marks from being dragged. I tore my clothes off and put them in the trash. Then I got in the shower, and as the hot water washed over me, I cried and cried.

How could I let this happen? When will all this shit stop? I got back into bed and cried myself to sleep again. It was a long weekend, so I didn't have to be back at work until Tuesday. I stayed in my room all weekend. I didn't answer the phone or the door.

Does this guy know me? Does he know what barracks I live in? Not taking any chances, I remained on high alert. I spent those next two days telling myself I had asked for it. I shouldn't have been drinking. I shouldn't have walked off alone. I had to go on as if it never happened. When Tuesday rolled around, I doctored my face up and went to work.

Of course the bruise was still visible, so when asked, I laughed it off, saying I got hit with a volleyball. No one was the wiser.

I went through all the motions of normal life. I got ready for and participated in my chief's initiation, but paid attention to my surroundings at all times. Then I started drinking again, trying to quiet the noise in my head. I thought I was surviving and this would be my secret, my private pain for the rest of my life.

Then a new female chief moved into my barracks. She must have seen something in me because she started asking questions—questions about if I had ever been raped. I broke down and told her that yes, I had. She told me it wasn't too late, and that I needed to report it. I was confused and didn't know if I could. She arranged for me to meet with one of the agents of the Naval Criminal Investigative Service.

Bam, it was like it was happening all over again. Questions, so many questions.

"What were you doing? Did you encourage this guy? Were you drunk? Did you start something you did not want to finish?"

Me: "What? Are you crazy? You think I wanted this to happen to me?"

They had me meet with someone to have a drawing done of the guy, who I hadn't really seen at all. Then they wanted to do a lineup of men. I couldn't do it. I just wanted to forget this ever happened. They continued to pressure me. I didn't want everyone to know. That's what happens when women report these things—everyone knows, and it becomes her fault. Nope, I wasn't going to let that happen. So I backed out. I couldn't wait for orders to get out of that place. I just wanted them to leave me alone!

I stuffed this behind that door to the room of pain in my heart. I locked the door (again) and told myself it would never be opened (again), but something like that doesn't just go away. It lingers, it eats at you, and it simmers just below the surface—like a volcano waiting to erupt. I have suffered from depression, and I have wanted to commit suicide several times. I have never told this to anyone else, not even my current husband.

I knew I needed help. I went to several counselors, but I was never able to unlock that door and tell my story. My last counselor told me that I needed to find a way to tell it, to release it and begin the healing process.

So, this is my story. Almost every word here has been extremely difficult for me to put on paper. Maybe someday I will be able to verbalize it, maybe not.

I managed to go on with my life, despite it all. I had a successful career in the navy; I was proud of my accomplishments and felt like a trailblazer. I had opportunities I never would have had if not for the more than twenty years I served.

But if I had a daughter or if a young girl asked me questions about being in the service, I believe I would be honest with her about the silence of women who have suffered military sexual trauma. I would tell her about the wonderful opportunities available, but also, I would say: Don't be naïve. Don't put yourself in a position to be compromised. Immediately shut down any man who attempts to harass you, and tell him it is not acceptable, and if it continues, you will report him.

Even if a woman does these things, there is no guarantee that she will not suffer violence or rape—no guarantee while in the service and no guarantee throughout her life. There is an ever-present culture of violence and misogyny in our society and throughout the world that has got to change. No one—man, woman, or child should ever have to suffer at the hands of another human being.

Do I regret my time in the service? No way! Life goes on, and sometimes you just have to try and love yourself.

What Did I Get Myself Into?

by Karin Marie Kalb

I stood in baggage claim after flying for more than twenty-four hours with three boys. We had just traveled from Idaho to the Caribbean, in January, and were still in our winter clothes. It was hot! My husband, John, was standing in a long line at the rental car counter, and I was trying to keep the boys under control. After being cooped up in planes for two days, they had lots of energy, but I was tired! So there I was, wondering, *what did I get myself into*?

For the first forty years of my life, I'd never lived more than two hundred miles from where I was born. We had a beautiful house. I had family and close friends, the boys were in a great school, and we were active in our church. It never occurred to me to want to live anywhere else, and frankly, just the thought of it scared me. I have always enjoyed staying firmly within my comfort zone, and I couldn't imagine moving somewhere that wasn't familiar, that didn't have a support system.

The previous year had been tough for our family. We lost John's parents within five days of each other. It was sudden and left us devastated. John had also been increasingly unhappy in his job. When he told me about an opportunity on St. Thomas, I was intrigued. We both liked the idea, so when they offered to fly us down for an interview, we quickly said yes.

During our three days on the island, we fell in love with it. The interview went well, and we went home hoping for an offer. While we waited to hear about the position, school started and life moved on, but I found that I wasn't the same. Before, I had been perfectly content in our family's home routine, but now I felt restless and uncertain. My mind had shifted. I didn't want to buy the boys snow gear; we wouldn't need it in the Caribbean. I started getting rid of things we didn't need, and I wasn't shopping in bulk as I had before. We couldn't take it with us, so why buy it?

I have always disliked the cold, and found myself really hating it as fall turned to winter. I wanted to be on a warm tropical island, not shoveling the driveway and freezing. Why hadn't we heard anything? I wanted to know, one way or the other. Then, the week before Thanksgiving, the offer came. They wanted John to start in the middle of January.

Then began the mad rush of the holidays, combined with the stress of packing a house and moving across an ocean! What should we take? What should we get rid of? What should go into storage? After weeks of sorting, packing, and cleaning with lots of help from amazing friends, we were done.

As I sat in the airport before we departed, I cried. I was excited to go, but it was also quite scary. What now? What would the local culture be like? Would we fit in? I knew we would be joining an expat community with support from John's new employers, but I wondered how we would integrate with the people of the island. Would they welcome us? I had never been an outsider before.

This was a significant departure from my comfort zone. Would we be able to find a house? How would the boys settle into their new school? I was worried that they might have trouble finding friends. They had always been in the same school and church, so they had never had to make much effort to find new friends. Would they know how?

We were leaving our oldest son in Idaho; he was a young adult and already living on his own. How would he do without us nearby? I already missed him. There were so many questions as we started this journey. I sat there at the gate with my boys around me, my mind whirling.

Finally, we made it to our temporary housing in a peaceful, lovely area facing the Yacht Haven Grande Marina. The condo was right on the water! We were happy to stay in such a beautiful place while we settled into island life and looked for a house. John's new employer was helpful and understanding. I was thankful that we didn't need to worry about his job during those first couple of weeks. We got the boys registered for school and set about starting our new life.

Although English is the main language spoken on St. Thomas, the West Indian people have their own unique way of speaking it. Usually it's the same words but with the emphasis on a different syllable. I did my best to pick up the rhythm, occasionally having difficulty understanding it. Once, we had someone come in to clean our house. When she was just about done, she asked me if we had enough "toe-ELLS." I had no idea what she had said, so I asked her to repeat the question. "Do you have enough toe-ELLS?" I still didn't have a clue until she pointed to a kitchen towel and said, "Toe-ELLS. Do you have enough?" The light bulb went on—towels! Duh. I felt stupid. Yes, we had enough toe-ELLS, thank you.

I was used to feeling like a member of our community, familiar with neighbors and shop owners and the people you typically greet in your weekly routine. Now everything and everyone was new and unfamiliar, foreign—and I was the foreigner. I have to admit, it was unsettling. I wanted to learn about the local culture and embrace it, but it was going to take time.

There was also the issue of driving. They drive on the left! My husband drove us everywhere during our first week, but then he went to work, and I had to take the wheel, literally. So, I took a deep breath, told the boys to be quiet because Mommy has to concentrate, and set off. John had told me it was just like following the leader, and it was—although on a bigger, much more stressful level.

St. Thomas is essentially one big mountain with curvy, steep roads. There are potholes everywhere, and the rules of driving on the island bear little resemblance to those in the United States. I learned through much trial and error, and I'm sure I angered quite a few other drivers. I also discovered that honking the horn is a separate language on the island that takes time to master. There are lots of little beeps going all the time, and I am never quite sure if they are directed at me. It became clear fairly quickly, though, that when you annoy another driver, the beep is long and loud. That one I know for sure.

I learned to drive in the rushed atmosphere of the States, so it was a challenge to slow down and enjoy the ride. From almost any road on the island, you can see the ocean, so whenever I found myself frustrated and stressed about traffic, I tried to take a breath and look at the beautiful azure sea.

I had an even tougher time adjusting to island shopping. There are no big box stores here, and the grocery stores are nothing like what I was used to. I grew up in a small town with big, bright, clean chain grocery stores that offer everything in one stop. Once Walmart came in, one-stop shopping took on a whole new meaning. The island offers nothing like that. The grocery stores were dark and dingy. Sometimes you had to blow the dust off the canned goods, and I always checked expiration dates. It wasn't uncommon to find sour milk in the dairy case.

There is no such thing as one-stop shopping for a family of five on St. Thomas. I had to go to a minimum of three stores each week. I vividly remember my first experience in one of those stores. I was still apprehensive about shopping on my own, but we needed groceries, so my youngest and I set out.

I hit the produce section first, and learned that since produce must travel over an ocean before reaching our local store, the first step was to set aside the moldy items to find something somewhat fresh. I was looking at the onions, with my son chatting away in the cart, when an older woman tried to move my cart, then yelled at me. "Move! I want to look at the onions!" I was stunned. I didn't know how to react. I decided I didn't need onions that badly, and moved on.

As we looked through the store, I was pleased to find some familiar things, but I was blown away by prices that were double, sometimes triple those in the States. This one shopping trip was taking so long, and I was growing tired from the stress of it. I finally headed to the registers, but when I put my groceries on the belt and tried to push my cart through, I accidentally bumped it into the candy shelf. Ok, I thought, I must have had it a little crooked. I adjusted it and tried again. Nope. It bumped into the other side. By this time, I was really confused. Finally, the clerk looked at me like I was an idiot, and yelled, "The carts don't fit! You have to take it around front!"

Of course, everyone turned and looked at me. I really had no idea what to do. Should I leave my groceries on the belt and take the cart to the front? Should I wait until the groceries are rung up and then move the cart? Thankfully, a nice young man took pity on me and told me that people usually leave the carts because they don't fit, and he takes care of them. I thanked him, paid for my groceries, and practically ran with my son to our car. Once I was safely inside, I lost it. I was sitting there in my jeep, sobbing, with my sweet little five year old in the back asking if Mommy was okay.

I felt so out of place and embarrassed that day. It made me wonder if I would ever fit in. But I have since learned which stores have what I need and the little tricks for shopping efficiently. I know where the workers are friendly (though I still get yelled at every once in a while), and I rarely go back to that first store.

The first six months on the island were like a blur. I remember someone telling me that it takes a good year to really settle into island life, and I found that to be true. Since that first time out on my own, I've met many warm, friendly, caring people on St. Thomas, and it has become my home. It was not long after our one year mark that I was asked how I like island life and if I missed living in the States. I took a moment to really think about it and realized that I love our little island. I really do.

We've had our share of challenging moments, but we have genuinely fallen in love with it. Our boys have been exposed to snorkeling, scuba diving, and sailing. My son has sailed a Hobie Cat across the bay to another island and eaten pizza off the pizza boat that is moored there. We have seen sea turtles and sharks and all sorts of marine life. The boys are in and out of the ocean like it's a pool. They have made good friends and have done so many things they couldn't have done in Idaho. Who would have thought that one of them would take a painting class on one of the top ten most beautiful beaches in the world? Or meet the USVI Olympic team? We were even featured on an episode of House Hunters International.

Now, we have the most wonderful friends here. I call them my island family. Many are transplants, like us. They have no actual family on the island, so we are family to each other. We go to the beach or meet for dinner often, and we are also there when anyone needs anything, from a babysitter to help with a flat tire.

Once, my youngest son came down with pneumonia, and my husband was away from the island. All it took was one text to my friends. They took the other boys to and from school all week. I had multiple calls and texts daily, asking if I needed anything. Even when I went to pick up his prescription, the pharmacist brought it out to my car, so I wouldn't have to wake him up and carry him in. This is just one example of local island neighbors who have been kind and caring. That's it, that's what I love.

The beaches are spectacular. I love watching the sun rise over the water every morning. I enjoy hearing birds outside my window every day—the roosters, not so much! But the people, our island family, they make it home. I feel blessed to have such wonderful people in my life. They make all of the little annoyances worth it. We laugh, cry, and drink rum together. What could be better than that?

I always thought of myself as a timid person. I like to feel safe, and I like things to stay the same. This was a tremendous life change for all of us, a departure way outside my comfort zone, and I've learned a few things about myself. I am still timid and sometimes shy, but I am brave, too. My husband and I took our boys and moved thousands of miles away. That takes guts, and I did it!

I've also learned that I am creative and resourceful. Many things aren't available on the island and I need to be flexible and think outside the box for everything from school projects to cooking dinner. I've learned that we don't need power to have a good time. The power goes out frequently, and although it's frustrating, it can be a good thing. We talk and play together much more when there is no TV or Internet to distract us. I've learned that familiar isn't always better.

I find myself looking forward to our next adventure whenever it comes. What will our next stop be? Back to the States? Switzerland? Italy? I don't know, but it sounds like fun—and I would never have thought that just a few years ago.

So, after three years, just what did I get myself into? I got into the best second family a person could have—island family. I got into learning new things about myself, my husband, and our boys. And last, but certainly not least, I got into knowing that life change can be scary, but not as scary as regret. We will never look back and say, "What if?" Instead, we will smile and say, "Remember when?"

Surviving & Thriving

by Markela Evett Morrell

"There is no greater agony than bearing an untold story inside you."

- Maya Angelou

I was born in Panama City, Panama, on March 19, 1965, to Tomas Reveas Morrell and Anita Yolanda Griffith. In my early years I lived with my maternal grandmother, Louise A. Griffith (aka Nell). This was at my mother's request, but I never knew why. Maybe it was about money.

My childhood is filled with happy memories—playing, attending church, going to the movies, hanging out at the beach. Since my mother and her siblings were grown and living elsewhere, I often had Grandma's whole house to myself: a side porch, back porch, and the option to sleep in whatever bedroom I wanted. There were mango, papaya, and breadfruit trees to climb—it was heaven.

I loved going to church, and celebrating birthdays and Christmas in Nell's home. No one had any problem with me. I would have been fine if they would have left me there.

When I was five or six, my mother left Panama and moved to the United States, and I was sent to live with Uncle Junior (my mom's oldest brother) and Aunt Amy, who is awesome. Amy's mom made wedding cakes, and boy, it was fun living in that house. The best times were when I got to go visit my dad. He worked on the Panama Canal and sometimes I would go with him to see the humongous ships—they fascinated me.

My dad's wife, Elena, is a wonderful woman; she always treated me as if I were her own child. I found out she was my dad's main girl even back when he was messing around on my mom. A few years after I was born, Dad and Elena had two children together, Manuel and Sherlena. Dad always taught us to be loving to one another and that no matter how far apart we might grow, we would always be brother and sisters. Manuel and Sherlena have always called me their sister, not half-sister. After Dad passed on, they even made sure that I got a fair share of what he left behind. To this day, they respect and love me, and call me to keep in touch. My siblings are good people.

When I was seven, I was moved again, to Aunty Baby's house. Aunty Baby is the cool aunt (my mom's youngest sister). I'm still not sure why I was moved to stay with her family, but remember often hearing arguments about money.

Aunty Baby had four boys; I was the only girl in the house. It was fun being a tomboy and running around with the boys. I lived with them until my mom came to take me back to the United States with her. Aunty Baby claims that she didn't want me to go, and it hurt her to see me leave. I was happy to go with my mom, but at the same time, very sad to leave my family in Panama.

At nine, I learned on my way to yet another new home that I had a stepfather and a brother and sister, Dimitri and Nikole. When I got to New York with Mom, we were all living together as a family, but I was treated like an outsider.

I was a dreamer in the land of opportunity, and my mother took her frustrations out on me in physical, verbal, and spiritual abuse. My body became a battlefield. The abuse was terrible—slaps, kicks, pinches, and beatings with bats, extension cords, or whatever was around. It sent me into shock. I was repeatedly told that I was a bad child, and felt as if I was going completely out of my mind. My life in Panama had been carefree and happy. How did my mother let me go from Panama to this?

One morning when I was ten years old, we were getting ready for church and I was unable to find one of my shoes. When I told my mother, she screamed that I had misplaced the shoe on purpose so that I wouldn't have to go to church. On the way there, she said I was the devil and I had nothing but evil in me. Later, Grandma Nell came to the United States, and at one point she lived with us. She tried to shield me from the beatings, but even she was not able to save me from her daughter's anger.

After I'd lived in the United States for a while, my mom had two more children, Gregorio and Hjordis, and I helped take care of them. There is still a strong bond between my little sister, Hjordis, and me.

When I was twelve, my mom became a Jehovah's Witness and things got crazy. We weren't allowed to play outside. We were forced to act like a happy family, but there was a lot of hidden violence in our home. My most vivid childhood memories are in that loud, angry household in Brooklyn, my mother screaming, calling me names, and putting me down. Sometimes she would lose control and beat all of us.

My siblings distracted me from all the problems in our home. My mom and stepdad had some serious fights—I had never witnessed fighting like that in my life in Panama. I had to run away from it and take all the kids into a bedroom and close the door.

As years went by, the fighting between my mom and stepdad got worse, and so did the beatings. I always wondered why this woman was constantly beating me. Eventually, I realized that a lot of this trouble was instigated by my half-sister, Nikole. She acted as if she were on my side and felt bad when I was beaten, but in fact, she was the one stealing and doing everything I was being blamed for. She was a jealous child. Now that I was there, she was not the oldest sister anymore, so she found ways to get me in trouble. I was not even allowed to speak Spanish because Nikole convinced my mom that it was not right for me to do so. How could one child have so much power over an adult? I felt like I was Cinderella, or Joseph in Genesis 37.

We moved a lot and went to many new schools. Each time, for the first four or five months, I was picked on and bullied. When I told my mother, she asked me what I had done to make them pick on me.

I was hoping school would be a window into a world outside my own. I loved modeling, running, singing, doing gymnastics, cooking, decorating, and doing so many other artistic things, but my mom would not allow me to do any school activities. Once I was offered a chance to train for the track and gymnastics teams. I was so excited. This was my dream! But my mother declined the offer. When I asked why, she said she didn't have time to waste with that, and she beat me for questioning her.

One day during the summer before seventh grade, I was working on a puzzle when a friend called. My mother flew into a rage and told me that I was never to have anyone call, and that I would never have any friends. I carried that feeling into adulthood and still have to fight against it today.

In the ninth grade, a girl (who claimed to be my friend) set me up to be gang raped by six guys while she watched. They tied my hands to bedposts. Music was blasting. I screamed, only to be hit in the face by my violators. All I could do was beg them to stop. The girl watched the entire time, saying she didn't like me and that I acted like I was better than others. I thought they would kill me, but finally, they let me go.

Back at school, the girl walked in front of me, laughing and telling other students in the schoolyard a different version. I was so angry, I grabbed her and began beating her. No one could get me off of her until the police came. We were both handcuffed and taken to a precinct across from school. After learning what had happened to me, the officers called an ambulance that took me to the hospital. They called my mom, and when she arrived, instead of helping or being concerned, she tormented me and blamed me for the rape. When we got home, she beat me. I was fourteen.

Eventually, my attackers were all caught and convicted, but I was destroyed. My life was never the same again. I was confused, afraid, alone, and desperate. I hated myself. I came to believe that I was insignificant, evil, and unworthy. I believed the very worst and thought, if only I was better, if only I'd been a good girl—but I was doing all that was good. How could they do this to me?

There was no one I could tell and no one to go to. God? Who is God? I didn't think He cared. There I was, going through all this, and He was not helping me! Why God, why don't you just take me? But, there was a voice of truth within me; it was faint, yet determined, urging me to survive.

By now, my mother's abuse had become routine. It was just part of my day. The only upside to her rages was that she wouldn't speak to me for a few days afterward, and the silence was calming.

Having said all this, I still love my mother—because it's natural to love your mother. I'm sure she made many sacrifices, but I can never forget the unfairness of it all, and I believe my sad story could have been prevented if the abuse had been dealt with early on. My mother used verbal and physical violence to express her anger and frustration, and she hid what she did very well. I tried bringing it to the attention of the church, but my mother, a Jehovah's Witness with folks looking up to her, made me look like a problematic, rebellious child. She is still in denial to this day, and the maternal side of my family still treats me like an outcast because of her. I stay away from most of them.

When I was fifteen years old, I met a boy who was nice to me. We talked a lot and became close. Eventually, I ran away from home. He was aware of the abuse I was suffering, but could not help, so he took me back home. When my mom let me in, I tried to apologize, but she told me to go pack my clothes. All I could do was cry. Then the doorbell rang. It was the police. They took me away and put me in a group home. I was there when I found out I was pregnant.

On August 17, 1981, my son was born. I was sixteen years old. My son and I were in foster care for a while, and then I made arrangements for him to live with my aunt. Once he was out of foster care and growing up in Panama, I knew he was safe. I needed to take care of myself. And I was a mess.

I had two nervous breakdowns. I saw a therapist for a while, but I could never forget everything I went through. From the time I was sixteen, I basically raised myself on the streets of New York City. I followed the wrong crowd and got into trouble. It seems I always put my trust in the wrong people, looking for love and acceptance in all the wrong places. I made a lot of mistakes that I've had to deal with in my grown-up life, and I knew that I would have to go backward in order to move forward. I had to examine the childhood that continued to cause me pain, to challenge the monsters living inside my head and defeat them with the truth of who I am.

As a survivor, I am continually uncovering the hidden wounds of my youth, and I suspect that there will always be parts of me I need to heal;

yet, I cannot help but see my life as a blessing. It is this very stuff, traumas and all, that gives me what I need to find my purpose in life. The pain of not having a loving mother and of being stripped of my innocence gives me so much to write about. It pushes me to grow and find my true self. It is the fuel that drives me to persist, no matter what comes my way.

This is the beginning of my journey. I am now healing and reconditioning my mind after years of cruelty and abuse. The people in and around my mother's home tore me down for thirty years, but God has me flying high, and the scenery is beautiful.

In 2012, I was pushing on, working hard, and dealing with life's disappointments. I made a conscious effort to surround myself with positive movers and shakers—it was then that God led me to 4 Real Women International (4RWI). It was time to start a different chapter of my life, to give back and be a leader. I wasted so much time being angry and rebellious, procrastinating and not finishing school, and just not caring. When I was in the group home, I did stupid things like shoplifting, but I am so thankful to God that I never got involved in drugs or prostitution, as many of the other girls did. I've made mistakes in my adult life, too. Life is complicated.

The 4 Real Women leadership academy allowed me to use my voice and helped me realize after all these years that what I went through was not my fault. 4 Real Women empowers and educates women who have suffered child abuse or domestic violence. 4RWI workshops help women who don't have a home or a job, those who haven't finished school, and women who have an abundance of stress with little hope. The programs teach that no matter what happens in life, it's okay to start over. Trained mentors and facilitators help girls and women regain self-esteem, create a healthy lifestyle, and (re)discover their purpose—supporting them in school as students, in business as rising professionals and entrepreneurs, and at home as daughters, sisters, wives, and moms. The overall 4RWI message is that with determination, a positive attitude, and a safe, encouraging environment, women can confront their fears, put the past behind them, and upgrade their skills to achieve confidence and not only succeed, but *lead*.

The 4RWI leadership academy was my first graduation (I cry just thinking of that day), and I feel no shame that I never finished school. I am so grateful to God for bringing Norka Lizette Blackman-Richards into my life. I wish she could see my heart. She made my journey through life so much clearer. She makes us rise! It is now 2017, and I, Markela Morrell, am 51 years old and in college getting a degree.

Being Still and Listening

by Penny James

The following is a brief excerpt from the upcoming autobiography by Penny James, *Zero Degrees of Separation*:

As a model for more than two decades, my experience living in poor-, middle-, and upper-class neighborhoods throughout the years, then getting away from their noise to quiet meditation in nature, gave me unique insight. My fashion media work while visiting Japan, Canada, Greece, Spain, France, Germany, Australia, Switzerland, Puerto Rico, Mexico, and small islands such as Cat Island, helped me to see that despite geographic and cultural borders, we are all one.

I mention each travel destination because living with people on their soil gave me knowledge of their diverse and original customs, cuisines, habits, and family patterns. This was tremendously grounding for me— an awakening. We all long for a stable home, an oasis of peace. As each place and its people became part of me, it left no doubt that we each have a unique role in shaping our shared world.

Temple Grandin, the author of *Thinking in Pictures, My Life With Autism*, was able to capture the yearning we all feel:

"I don't want my thoughts to die with me. I want to have done something . . . I want to know that my life has meaning . . . I'm talking about things at the very core of my existence."

Partner Miscasting

My husband and I struggled with our marriage as I worked at my newfound sobriety. We went to one more therapy session together and were told our relationship was father/daughter, rather than one of two equals, and it would have to change if our marriage was going to work. (It had gotten to the point that I would ask him if I could go to the store.) I remembered his mom and dad coming to visit in the early days of our marriage. They were part of the reason I had fallen for him in the first place. His mother was strong and independent; his father sweet and caring. They were the best of him, and they were lovely to me. They showed me attention and affection that rarely existed in my own childhood, and it meant the world to me.

As he and I worked on our hands and knees, caring for the rose garden during one of his parents' visits, it was sunny and my husband's breath was riding a happy whistle. Through all of the highs and lows, through the fog of my drinking and pain of recovery, I still clung to the hope that we would someday be old, walking down a path together, holding hands.

One day, and I don't know which one it was, the music died. There are things that happen in life that defy explanation. As drugged as I was during the seventies and early eighties, there was a clean, clear energy that allowed me to take in certain information.

Reliving and writing about this time has been difficult because I was scattered, shattered in so many pieces, broken. There were no quick fixes. There is nothing sexy about getting sober. One doesn't stop using drugs and drinking, and then everything suddenly gets normal. It took years to unscramble my brain before I was comfortable enough with myself to build a new life. It took listening to other people's stories, learning from them, and then slowly putting mine back together.

The good news for anyone reading this book who thinks they might have a drinking problem: you can get the best therapy and help that money can buy by joining AA, and it won't cost a penny. It's a fact. I've lived it. And if you can accept this gift, life will eventually blossom beyond your wildest dreams.

The Mercedes

I was no longer my husband's property and was not allowed to touch his property. The new black Mercedes was the first car that I hadn't contributed to monetarily. I remember looking down from the guest bedroom of our home as he would leave for work every morning. His ritual was wiping it down with a cloth until there wasn't a speck of dust. He was now at the top of his career after working diligently for almost twenty years.

Why did I keep watching him through the window long after dark heaviness had settled around my heart? What was I feeling? Now I know it didn't have much to do with him. It came from a much earlier time in childhood when I was crying out for help.

Sleep finally came . . . knowing help wouldn't be coming. A family pattern had been set up for abandonment. Destiny. I had chosen the perfect partner. At this point I had been excised, like a tumor. The scalpel blade was sharp, cutting through all the layers of time we had spent together. It wouldn't be long before I watched him drive away one final morning. Our life together was over.

I would no longer depend on the wrong people, places, and things that once moved me into emotional, dead-end madness. In the future I would choose to never again desperately wait for a telephone call that would never ring. It was empowering to realize we can choose to never be stuck counting on someone and feeling let down when we need them the most, whether in love or in business.

I had finally settled down enough to listen to the clarifying whisper instead of falling victim to the confusing, superficial noise of my own mind. The late singer/songwriter, Portia Nelson, described the transition in five short stanzas:

I

I walk down the street.
There is a deep hole in the sidewalk. I fall in.
I am lost, I am helpless.
It isn't my fault. It takes forever to find my way out.

II

I walk down the same street.
There is a deep hole in the sidewalk.
I pretend I don't see it. I fall in again.

I can't believe I am in the same place.
But, it isn't my fault.
It still takes a long time to get out.

III
I walk down the same street.
There is a deep hole in the sidewalk. I see it is there.
I still fall in . . . it's a habit.
My eyes are open.
I know where I am. It is my fault.
I get out immediately.

IV
I walk down the same street.
There is a deep hole in the sidewalk.
I walk around it.

V
I walk down another street.

Acknowledgements

First and foremost, thanks to the twelve brave women who have shared your stories, for believing in this book and for your willingness to contribute. You are all stars.

To the amazing women of 4RWI, this book started because you all make me want to be a better woman. Thank you for your enthusiasm and support for this idea from the beginning.

To Marion Bieber, genius designer and creative sounding board in all graphic matters, I don't know what I would do without you, and hope I never have to find out.

Andy Kalish at Waterfall Web Solutions, you are the most patient, gifted website developer any small business owner can hope for. For early mornings, late nights, and weekends while this came together, thank you doesn't seem to cover it. You are a gem.

To Peter Cyngot, for signing on in the eleventh hour and running with my half-formed vision, you are wonderful.

Greg Ioannou of Iguana Books, Publaunch, and Colborne Communications, you are a constant source of support, encouragement, and education. Your help made this possible.

Special cheers to the fierce, fabulous editing and production crew at Iguana/Colborne in Toronto: Paula Chiarcos, Holly Warren, Kathryn Willms, Jen Albert, and also Meghan Behse—you ladies saved me when I was forced to accept that help is a good thing. You each played your part and the book is better because of you.

Chief Joseph Werner, for being at my back and in my corner through highs and lows, for richer or poorer, in sickness and in health - all just this year. I'm so lucky you took the vows seriously. You are the love of my life.

And last but far from least, this book is for my mother, Esther Kallman, whose memory will continue to guide and inspire me for the rest of my days. XX

CPSIA information can be obtained
at www.ICGtesting.com
Printed in the USA
BVHW040258121218
535228BV00033BA/1792/P